Inspirational Authors

I'd also like to thank the authors of some great books that shaped my thinking:

> *Tom Emerick & Al Lewis (Cracking Health Costs), Dr. Atul Gawande (Being Mortal), David Goldhill (Catastrophic Care), Dr. Marty Makary (Unaccountable), Dr. Robert Pearl (Mistreated), Sam Quinones (Dreamland), Cathryn Jakobson Ramin (Crooked), Elisabeth Rosenthal (An American Sickness), Paul Shoemaker (Can't Not Do), Nassim Taleb (Antifragile), John Torinus (The Company that Solved Healthcare), and many others.*

I'm thankful for those I follow on Twitter—twitter.com/chase-dave/following. I constantly weed and feed that list with a self-imposed 100 follow limit. This makes it my most useful tool for keeping up with the industry.

Policy & Politics

Leaders in the policy and political arena are included in the list of people I follow on Twitter, but there are others worth calling out by name:

> *Michael Cannon, Peter Grant, Nick Hanauer, Dr. Farzad Mostashari, and Governor Tommy Thompson. Also noteworthy are politicians such as Governor Jay Inslee, Senator Bill Cassidy, and others who have worked across party lines on initiatives such as making Direct Primary Care more available.*

The Book Team

Lauren Phillips led the book's editing effort. Her depth in health care didn't hamper her ability to make the book readable for people outside of health care. She was a delight to work with.

W9-AAA-847

I also want to specially thank my partner in the Health Rosetta, Sean Schantzen. Without him, there's no way I could advance the Health Rosetta ecosystem like we are. He's an unofficial editor and has added critical depth to the book, uses his legal background to keep me out of hot water, oversees our investing, launche the Health Rosetta certification program, and has been key to executing our strategy to grow the Health Rosetta ecosystem. Perhaps most importantly, he's fundamentally driven by a similar mission as I am. Scaling broad adoption of simple, proven, non-partisan fixes to our health care system has become the thing he can't not do.

The Fuel to My Fire

I wouldn't be fully candid if I didn't mention the nearly daily fuel I receive from the stories of organizations and individuals acting with impunity to protect their interests at great expense to society. Here are just two examples.

1. Executives at one of the largest tax-exempt, faith-based hospitals systems in the country threatening electoral retaliation against the mayor of a city. Why? The mayor wanted to provide far better primary care to employees than the hospital system was providing. This would have allowed the city to balance its budget and provide better services to citizens.
2. An executive at one of the largest insurance companies in the country knowingly turning a blind eye to literally billions of dollars of fraud (see Chapter 7 for details) being perpetrated against the employees and employers they process claims for. One of the impacted companies (a heartland manufacturer) laid off 10,000 workers—many of which could have been saved if not for the $100s of millions of clearly fraudulent claims paid by the company.

The Best Part of My Life

Last, but certainly not least—my family. Almost everything I write goes past Coleen for review. If something I write isn't comprehensible, it's usually because I didn't run it by her. Our kids, Abby & Cam, warn people to not bring up health care with me unless they have hours of available discussion time.

They have heard more about health care than anyone should have to, yet still have the sense of humor to give me grief about it. They may not know it, but a core reason I'm maniacal about building a much improved health ecosystem is that I want to do my part to leave them with a much better health ecosystem than when I arrived. God has blessed me with a great family and great kids. I'm on a mission to ensure everyone has the same opportunities for full health that we have.

FOREWORD

Brian Klepper

One of American health care's deep mysteries has been employers' and unions' reluctance to challenge the health care industry's excesses that deeply threaten their finances, our lives, and our country. At least some people and organizations in every health care sector—drug and device companies, care provider organizations, insurers and health plan administrators, health IT firms—extract far more money than the value they create. This is even though many, if not most, individuals in the health care industry are good people working within an enormously broken, yet immensely powerful, system.

Health care's lobbying grip on national and local policy, and its immense market strength make it seem all but unstoppable. In 2009, the health care industry spent $1.2 billion to influence the Affordable Care Act.[1] Even as health care costs have soared, the public and private employers that pay most of the tab for 150 million Americans have largely accepted this as unavoidable. This book shows that tackling costs *while* improving care isn't just unavoidable, but simpler to do than you think.

Back in 1980, the editor of the *New England Journal of Medicine*, Arnold Relman, warned of a medical industrial complex that now dwarfs the military industrial complex that President Eisenhower feared.[2] Almost 40 years later, it is astonishing to appreciate how serious the impacts of this are throughout our society.

- Wasteful health care spending consumes 79 percent of household income growth, leaving just 21 percent for everything else.[3] This, more than nearly anything, is destroying the American dream.
- Musculoskeletal disorders consume 4 to 4.5 percent of the *entire* U.S. GDP.[4] We perform about double the musculoskeletal treatments of other industrialized countries, yet get no better health outcomes.[5] This means ~2 percent of our entire economy is wastefully consumed by just one sliver of our health care system. Benefits purchasers that have tackled this one area have reduced their total spending by 4 to 11 percent.
- A 2015 study found that two-thirds of cancer drugs approved by the FDA from 2008 to 2012 have no evidence that they actually work.[6] "Our results show that most cancer drug approvals have not been shown to, or do not, improve clinically relevant endpoints," the study's authors wrote, which is researcher-speak for "most cancer drugs don't work."
- U.S. companies are at a 9 percent cost disadvantage in international markets compared to countries like Germany, Australia, and Korea as a result of our higher spending

U.S. health care is complicated, powerful, and doing everything possible to maintain the status quo. That said, meaningful change generally finds its genesis in small, seemingly insignificant acts. When Dave Chase's columns first appeared on the *Forbes* website, his breezy, attention-grabbing style and shockingly indisputable facts about health care's outrages and solutions resonated with employer, benefits, insurer, and care provider communities looking for what's possible.

Dave has connected the health care dots in a highly insightful and actionable new way, clearly describing:

1. The root causes of dysfunction
2. The gravity of their implications
3. The practical solutions that provide a way out
4. What rules a new health care paradigm must adhere to

For CEOs, CFOs, and benefits executives, the strategies here are refreshingly straightforward and proven approaches to a seemingly intractable problem. They reduce health care costs *while* improving the quality of care.

Dave's tireless devotion to laying out the health care industry's problems and solutions is fueling a new energy around out-of-the-box, high-value programs and practical solutions. Perhaps more than anyone else, his thoughtful optimism in an all-but-hopelessly corrosive health care industry has become a rallying point for many Americans eager to build a new health care system based on transparency, evidence, and accountability.

It is hard to imagine a more worthwhile goal than that.

Brian Klepper, PhD, is a health care analyst and principal of Worksite Health Advisors, based in Orange Park, Florida.

A NOTE FROM A FELLOW TRAVELER

Tom Emerick

Author's Note: *Addressing misdiagnosis and overtreatment in cancer, musculoskeletal procedures, organ transplants, and other high-cost areas has a greater impact on patients than any blockbuster drug. Tom Emerick has more experience with these types of claims than most, if not all, benefits leaders. He was Walmart's Global VP of benefits and ran benefits at Burger King, British Petroleum, and American Fidelity. He's the author of Cracking Health Costs and created one of the first centers of excellence programs for large employers, subsequently making it accessible for any self-insured employer. He's been walking the path this book lays out for decades.*

When I travel around the U.S. giving speeches I often ask for a show of hands of people who have had relatives harmed by a major misdiagnosis, bad surgery, botched treatment plan, etc. Nearly every hand in the room always goes up and everyone is always incredibly surprised to see this. I then share that if they know ten people who have died of cancer, likely three of those ten were misdiagnosed and given a useless or harmful treatment plan. Jaws drop, but it's true.

I follow this with "how are we spending $3 trillion on a health care system that is harming so many people?" How is this happening? We've all seen bad medical events with our own families and friends, but we don't realize how common and costly it is. This is also the core insight behind what's wrong with the U.S. health care system.

I've had the unique experience of being behind the scenes for more than 30 years. This has let me identify seven high-level systemic problems with the US health care system. All are the result of various flawed incentives Dave covers in the following pages. These problems enormously damage our country, both individually and collectively. This book addresses these issues and practical solutions in a systemic way I've not found elsewhere.

1. Lack of accountability

Health care providers aren't accountable to anyone for the quality of care provided in the U.S. A clinician can misdiagnose 20-40 percent of patients, which many do, yet nobody prevents it or stops them. The biggest care quality failure is misdiagnosis. Anything that follows harms you and your wallet. Data shows that misdiagnosis rates in some categories of major care are 20-40 percent! We have an epidemic of misdiagnosis.

2. Status quo lobbying power

Health care institutions in America are very powerful. Few, if any, sectors of our economy have more powerful lobbies at both the national and local levels than health care providers and health insurers. They have $3 trillion reasons to protect the status quo and spend more than anyone to protect it.

3. The American health care exceptionalism fallacy

There is a fallacy in the U.S. that we have the best health care. This is simply not true. We may have the easiest access to care or the most providers in certain categories. However, the cost and quality of this doesn't really stack up to our peer countries in any critical systemic metric. Our health care is twice as expensive with significantly worse results.

4. Limited individual purchaser influence

The individuals and corporations that pay for over half of health care lack the individual power or influence to offset that of our collective health care institutions. Our government pays the other half, yet even Medicare and Medicaid do a poor job of managing many issues, including the widespread misdiagnosis and over-treatment of patients discussed in this book.

5. Widespread conflicts of interest

The world of health care insurers, providers, vendors, buyers, brokers, and advisors is a bizarre world rife with conflicts of interest we just wouldn't accept elsewhere in society. For example, benefit managers generally hire benefit consultants paid by health insurers and providers. This is a textbook conflict of interest. If Fred hires Bob to sue Joe, Joe would be off his rocker to hire Bob to defend him. Yet this kind of nuttiness is the default approach throughout the purchasing, administration, and delivery of health care in America. Enough is enough.

6. Poor internal financial oversight

Health care plans are one of the biggest areas of spending and financial risks facing public and private employers, yet they've been placed in the hands of human resources managers. Taking care of employees is in HR's DNA and many are very good at it. Unfortunately, this same trait makes many of them poor benefits managers, risk assessors, and financial analysts. Many just have not made the necessary decisions to maximize the quality and minimize the cost of health benefits.

This isn't from a lack of solutions. They exist. They give employees better quality care, save employees out of pocket spending, and save employers money. Many HR managers are just not willing to shake up the status quo. Alas, the status quo needs to be shaken up badly.

7. *Reimbursement is more a wealth transfer than an economic transaction*

Expense reimbursement models in health care are not really economic transactions. If a consumer goes to a doctor who treats the consumer, but is paid by a third-party—an employer, insurer, or government entity—this is more a wealth transfer than a classic economic transaction. Market economics do not apply when third parties pay consumers' bills. Yet this is how health insurance works.

This book will explain these problems and the root causes behind them in detail, then offer you common sense ways to take control of health care costs and improve the quality of care your employees receive.

It is do or die time. If you think it wise to save our country and health care system, things need to change and change now.

INTRODUCTION

The U.S. middle class has gone backwards financially in the last 20 years. The culprit is our health care system. This was the conclusion of a groundbreaking 2013 RAND study, which found that:[7]

- Health care expenditures, including insurance premiums, out-of-pocket expenditures, and taxes devoted to health care, nearly doubled between 1999 and 2009.
- This increase substantially eroded what an average family has to spend on everything else, leaving them with only $95 more per month than in 2007.
- Had health care costs tracked the Consumer Price Index, rather than outpacing it, an average American family would have had an additional $450 per month— more than $5,000 per year—to spend on other priorities.

We all know health care is broken. Yet we all believe that most health care professionals—at least the ones we know—are amazingly talented and altruistic. How can this be? The problem isn't the people, it's systemic: our health care system is crushing the altruism right out of physicians and nurses. At the same time, it's crushing the hopes and dreams of middle-income families.

Before you think hope is lost, I want to make one critical point. Why read this book at all? Isn't reducing health care costs like solving Middle East peace? No, it's not, despite what we've all heard over and over. Push this myth out of your mind forever.

This book's singular purpose is to persuade you to make a powerful mindset shift. You can improve your organization's bottom line, your employees' bottom line, and improve the quality of health care your employees receive. This book will show how and get you started down the path.

I've seen all types of organizations make the shift and create amazing results. Large and small. Public and private. All across our country. Following suit just requires making the shift and following through.

Step one of the shift is to accept that you run a health care business. It's likely your second largest operating expense after payroll. Just ask your CFO. You'd probably prefer not to run this business, but it's there, whether you like it or not. Step two is to act and stick with it.

To help persuade you to make this mindset shift, here are a few major ways it will benefit your business, employees, bottom line, community, and country.

1. **Help save our country and communities** – As we'll discuss in more detail, waste in health care's status quo is running our country off a cliff. It's a primary cause for personal bankruptcies, broken public budgets, wage stagnation, and much more. If we don't make the shift, health care could consume all household income in less than 20 years.

2. **Take better care of your employees** – Every day, you make decisions that affect the lives of your employees and their families. I know the pressure. I've been there as an entrepreneur and executive. I also know that making the shift is a uniquely impactful way to put our money where our mouth is when we say our people are our greatest asset. Doing so leads to a higher-performing, more satisfied workforce.

3. **Materially improve your financial performance** – Health care spending is likely one of the last major buckets of operational expenses you haven't already intensely optimized. Reducing your spend using the approaches in this book can tangibly improve your financial performance, freeing resources

to improve wages, R&D, exit values, market caps, and more. Plus, the savings are recurring and compound over time.

I suspect the above reasons are more than enough to persuade you to make this essential mindset shift. Just in case they're not, let's go negative for a second. If you're already self-insured or plan to become so, emerging ERISA fiduciary duty issues we'll discuss could potentially create personal liability for you. You're likely to avoid this if you make the mindset shift and act on it.

There's really no reason to not make the shift. It's better for you, your employees, your community, and your country. And the good news is that not only is it possible, there are many examples to show the way. Let's get started.

So How Did We Get Here?

Why is health care so broken? Following the money is a good place to start. Our problems started with tax policy in the 1940s. During WWII, we had wage controls, but employer-paid benefits didn't count as wages. To attract employees, employers started offering more and more health benefits without paying attention to what these benefits cost. This is our original sin. It could also be our fount of redemption.

Over time, this practice sheltered us from the true cost of the care we buy, creating enormous dysfunction in what care we pay for and how we pay for it. We ended up focusing on a certain type of high-technology, acute medical care—which we financially reward far more than lower-level preventive and chronic care—without regard for the quality of the outcomes or value of the care. Because what difference does it make? Most of us get our care paid for by our employer or a government entity, who are just as ignorant about the true costs as we are. And here's the kicker: Most doctors and hospitals don't even know what it really costs to provide care because no one has held them accountable for such a long time.

This has big consequences. Our system's financial incentives aren't aligned with the outcomes we want, which most of us define as staying healthy in the first place and receiving high quality care when we need it, while still being able to afford and live a satisfying life. Instead, over decades, our health care system has made millions of small decisions to increase the quantity of care provided, which increases revenue, resulting in hyperinflating costs. Ultimately, we undervalue what keeps us healthy.

It's a sad equation: Poor financial incentives + we all want care + decades of small decisions = where we are today. The Kaiser Foundation found that "[s]ince Medicare passed, per capita [health care] spending has grown more than 50-fold. This far outstrips per capita spending on all other goods and services by at least 5 times."[8] The trend is only accelerating. Figure 1 is from the *Wall Street Journal* and shows that health care takes 25 percent more of middle-income household spending than in 2007, just ten years ago.

The Annual Benefits Kabuki Dance

Much of this dire situation is due to what benefits expert Craig Lack calls the annual kabuki dance of employers and health plans, which he described to me in a memorable conversation. Lack, CEO of the consulting firm ENERGI and co-author of *Think and Grow Rich Today*, says employers have been led to believe the best they can hope for is merely a less bad rate increase—despite the fact that there has been little to no increase in the underlying costs of medicine. Lack has said the following about this issue.

> Every year, CFOs ask their human resources (HR) team for a budget increase target. The overburdened and risk-averse nature of HR at most organizations is to preserve the status quo. The insurance companies know this and typically come in with an increase of 11-14 percent; the insurance brokers know this and "negotiate" a less bad increase, staying

A Bigger Bite

Middle-class families' spending on health care has increased 25% since 2007. Other basic needs, such as clothing and food, have decreased.

Percent change in middle-income households' spending on basic needs (2007 to 2014)

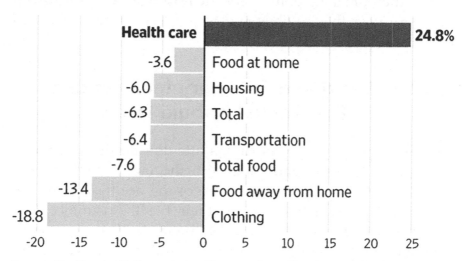

Sources: Brookings Institution analysis of Consumer Expenditure Survey, Labor Department

THE WALL STREET JOURNAL.

Figure 1. Source: "Burden of Health-Care Costs Moves to the Middle Class," Wall Street Journal, August 25, 2016.[9]

below the CFO's budget, and there you have it. Check the box, health care can be put to bed. See you next year. That's what passes for health care risk management at far too many organizations.

This system has continued because of two directives CEOs have long given HR: Keep people happy and don't get us sued. This may have made sense when health care benefits were a small percentage of the company's budget, but decades of hyperinflating costs have made it the second or third largest expense. Also, it's hard to make the argument that a company is keeping employees happy when health insurance has the lowest customer satisfaction of any industry and high deductible plans have suddenly become the norm.

I'm regularly asked to speak to benefits consultants, business coalitions, nonprofit associations, and public-sector organizations about how to tackle this situation. The overriding sentiment I find is that organization executives and benefits leaders have reached their breaking point. They are no longer willing to accept that every year they're obligated to get less and pay more for health benefits.

The Legal and Fiduciary Implications of The Annual Kabuki Dance

While we rightfully pay enormous attention to the Obamacare exchanges, Medicare, and Medicaid, the fact is that employers collectively pay the largest share of the health care tab and non-retirees overwhelmingly get their health insurance from work.[10] If health care's status quo is the immediate cause of the economic depression of lower-income and middle-class workers, the primary underlying cause is this hidden-in-plain-view Kabuki dance.

The issue goes far beyond just a poor process. There is growing discussion that the way health benefits dollars have been managed could be a breach of fiduciary duty under ERISA (the Employee Retirement Income Security Act of 1974), which governs most health plans. ERISA regulates both health and retirement benefits plans. It requires plan trustees to prudently use plan money for the benefit of plan beneficiaries, i.e., their employees. Overall, employers do this well in retirement benefits plans, but are seriously bad at it in health benefits plans.

To understand how this issue could play out, it's worth looking at what's happened in a highly-analogous context, 401(k) plan litigation. Here's an example. Employees of Edison International brought a class action suit against the company, alleging that Edison breached its fiduciary duties by offering participants in the 401(k) plan retail share classes of mutual funds when lower-priced institutional share classes were available. The employees won a unanimous verdict at the U.S. Supreme Court. There are some legal issues that prevent this exact type of plan beneficiary suit, but there are similar strategies being developed now that could be far more successful. These strategies could create personal liability implications for officers and directors. It's still early, but we've been following the issue enough that it's high on our radar at Health Rosetta. This issue could change rapidly as cases are filed.

A broader analogy shows the absurdity of such low expectations for those we rely on to help us provide health care benefits. My partner, Sean Schantzen, is a former practicing securities attorney who is relatively new to health care. He's pointed out that someone in financial services could face serious consequences, even jail, for not disclosing the sort of financial and non-financial conflicts of interest and incentives that are standard operating procedure in health care benefits purchasing and administration. For example, securities laws require brokers to fully disclose all financial compensation. Investment advisors must go beyond this and act as fiduciaries of their clients, They must act in their clients' best interests and can only place their money in investments suitable to each client's circumstances. The recently adopted Fiduciary Rule heightens these requirements even more. Those who don't meet these standards face serious consequences. By comparison, benefits brokers rarely fully disclose compensation or conflicts, such as cash bonuses for keeping 90 percent of their clients in disadvantageous arrangements with specific insurance carriers.[11] Just like we'd never accept our financial advisor not disclosing how they get paid on an investment before making an investment, we shouldn't make one of the single largest expenditures in our budgets without similar expectations.

One idea we've discussed with others is to require that ERISA health benefits plan dollars be subject to the same fiduciary practices as ERISA plan retirement plan dollars. Technically this is already required, but it's not general practice. There are uncertainties and complexities to this approach, particularly around developing critical safe harbors for employers. However, it's a high-potential path to providing protection to directors and officers, removing widespread lack of transparency and conflicts of interest, and raising the bar for how we buy such a critical resource.[12]

The Health Rosetta

I believe the Health Rosetta is the way forward. The Health Rosetta is an ever-evolving collection of principles and best practices that I and many like-minded professional colleagues have put together that's a blueprint for sustainably reducing costs and improving care. It's built on real-life successes, not theory. It simplifies the path for you to achieve similar results.

In the old model of health care, the supply side dictated the pricing and terms. Today, forward-looking organizations refuse to leave these areas unmanaged. The wisest are turning health care costs, which many view as a liability, into a source of competitive advantage. They have found they can reduce spending by 20 percent or more per capita while providing better benefits than 99 percent of the workforce. In other words, the best way to slash health care costs is to improve the quality of those benefits. The Health Rosetta makes it easier to follow these leaders.

The nonprofit Health Rosetta ecosystem's mission is to accelerate adoption of the Health Rosetta. It focuses on practical, nonpartisan fixes to how we pay for care, what we buy, and how we manage benefits. It helps public and private employers and unions reduce health benefits costs while providing better care for the 150 million Americans who receive health benefits through their jobs.

The focus of this book is on nongovernment paid health care. However, the Health Rosetta isn't employer-specific or even U.S. specific, for that matter. As I've spoken with people around the U.S. and world, it's clear that no country is without problems in how it purchases health care. Perhaps the biggest missed opportunity at the state and federal level is that the public sector is a large employer itself, representing a broad cross-section of society. The fact is public sector employers have all the same opportunities as private sector employers to greatly improve the value they receive.

Broadly speaking, the two biggest problems in the U.S. health care system are pricing failure (no correlation between price and health outcomes) and overtreatment. These problems are pervasive in both publicly and privately funded health care benefits. Policy makers would be wise to test and prove their models of reform with the public sector workforce. Fortunately, there are widespread examples of success they can follow. The Health Rosetta aggregates these into an understandable blueprint.

Here are a few of the Health Rosetta's foundational components.

- **Value-based primary care.** Properly conceptualized and incentivized primary care is the front line of defense against downstream costs.
- **Concierge services.** Navigating health care is complex, even for those of us in the industry. Employees need access to trusted, aligned resources.
- **Active ERISA plan management.** Employers deeply manage budgets in every other area of spend. Why not health benefits? Internal fiduciary oversight is critical.
- **Transparent medical markets.** Cost and quality are often inversely correlated in health care. Focusing on better quality and outcomes is the path to lower costs. This is particularly true for addressing high-cost outlier claims that make up the majority of spending.
- **Payment integrity.** Ensuring claims are paid correctly and tackling fraud is a critical step to high-performance benefits.
- **Transparent pharmacy benefits.** Purchasers need true transparency of data to control decision-making.

So, if the fixes already exist, why isn't everyone using them?

Health care's redemption is a classic example of solutions hidden in plain sight. Remember the *The Big Short* and *Moneyball?* As noted business consultant Ric Merrifield, author of *Rethink: A Business Manifesto for Cutting Costs and Boosting Innovation*, has pointed out, the films' shared theme is that in the face of a mountain of evidence, no one paid attention. Wall Street and federal regulators didn't downgrade the credit ratings of mortgage-backed securities, and no one paid attention to on-base percentage, even when the issues were right in front of them. The same goes for health care.

I think of health care as being in a similar place and following a similar path as the banking industry in the early and mid-2000s that partially led to the 2008 financial crisis. My hope is that this book will contribute to a health care turnaround more profound and longer lasting than that in banking.

A Note on Reading the CEO's Guide

The first two sections of this book, *The Current Situation* and *How and Why Employers Are Getting Fleeced*, explore in detail the case presented in this introduction, helping you understand specifically what has gone wrong with health care and what the consequences are to your employees, your organizations, our communities, and our country.

The last two sections, *Doing It Right* and *Health Rosetta*, will step you through key solutions you can start implementing immediately.

Throughout, you will find case studies of employers that have already achieved significant success implementing Health Rosetta components. The goal of these is to show how creative application of select strategies can be highly successful. Just copying them whole cloth is unlikely to work. You have to build a model that works for your geography, employees, claims experience, cost structure, and other variables.

Before we dive in, I want to cover a couple of issues to help you navigate the book. First, feel free to jump around. Each chapter generally stands on its own.

Second, I've tried to simplify the enormous complexity of our health care system. This means I'll skim or skip certain topics to avoid rabbit holes.

Third, health care always seems to use ten different words for essentially the same thing, each with some supposed slight variation in meaning that isn't even consistently used by those of us in the industry. To minimize confusion, I generally use consistent terminology in key topics.

- **People.** I use a couple different terms depending on context. *Individual* is the default. *Patient* is for people receiving care. *Member* or *employee* refer to individuals from a health plan's or employer's perspective.
- **Provider organization and clinician.** These terms cover the people and entities that provide health care services. This includes doctors, nurses, hospitals, health systems, and anyone else that provides health care services.
- **Insurance company or carrier.** These cover the organizations that provide insurance and/or self-insured plan administration services
- **Health plan.** This covers a specific health benefits plan, whether fully-insured or self-insured.
- **Plan administrator.** This is the organization that performs noninsurance pieces of a health plan, like claims adjudication. It includes Administrative Services Organizations (ASO) tied to insurance companies and independent Third Party Administrators (TPA). I use these more specific terms when distinguishing between the two.
- **Benefits broker, consultant, and advisor.** *Broker* describes those operating under the status quo, highly-conflicted approach to purchasing health benefits. *Advisor* or *consultant* are used to describe those operating under the modern, high-value, transparent approach. These three terms are often used

interchangeably in the real world, so typically aren't sufficient to identify high-value people and firms.

- **Workplace wellness program.** The term *wellness* has been co-opted by a large industry of vendors that largely sell no or negative ROI products. I'm a fan of the concept of wellness, i.e., well-being, just not these types of programs. I use this more specific term to refer to these programs.

Fourth, a couple chapters were primarily written by other experts I admire. Their names appear at the beginning of these chapters to easily identify them.

Finally, I've attempted to ensure every critical point, especially the more controversial ones, is well-cited. However, some sources are private conversations with other industry insiders who are uncomfortable being publicly cited. As a result, some citations for some points refer to private conversations and a few aren't cited.

To learn more, read on or visit healthrosetta.org

For ongoing insight, best practices, and updates, join the Health Rosetta newsletter at healthrosetta.org/employers.

Part I

The Current Situation

*A*s many of us have experienced in our professional lives, great
opportunities often come from adversity, problems, and setbacks.
*While it's hardly breaking news that there are problems in health care,
the extent of the collateral damage that is a direct byproduct of these
problems is less well known. This part of the book goes beyond the visible parts of our present situation to explore the underlying dynamics
and incentives behind many of these problems and the extent of collateral damage.*

*Most people have a fundamental misunderstanding of the pressures
that drive the health care industry. Those pressures have a profoundly
negative financial and health impact on your organization and employees. However, there is good news in our current situation. Despite what
you've heard, unit prices are flat in most of health care. Plus, millennials are now the largest chunk of the workforce and are changing their
world in ways that hold great promise for health care.*

CHAPTER 1

AMERICA HAS GONE TO WAR FOR FAR LESS

One definition of an economic depression is two or more years of income decline. Since the middle class has seen wages decline over the last 20 years after adjusting for inflation (see Figure 2), they have been experiencing a depression for nearly twenty years. Here's why.

Employers spend more on payroll than ever, yet virtually the entire increase has gone to health care costs, as Rand concluded in their report, *How Does Growth in Health Care Costs Affect the American Family?*[13] In many cases those costs have literally taken all of the payroll increases for middle class employees. In Mobile, Alabama last year, the Public Education Employees Health Insurance Plan board voted to raise health care insurance premiums for families, from $177/month to $307/month. This promptly ate up the state-approved 4 percent pay raise for employees that make less than $75,000 a year.[14]

Both employees and employers (public and private) bear the burden of these huge premium increases.

Accurate Box Co. CEO Lisa Hirsh said that 25 years ago health care benefits were 5 percent of an employee's total compensation at her company. Today, that cost can be 30, 40, or even 50 percent of total compensation. "When family health care costs

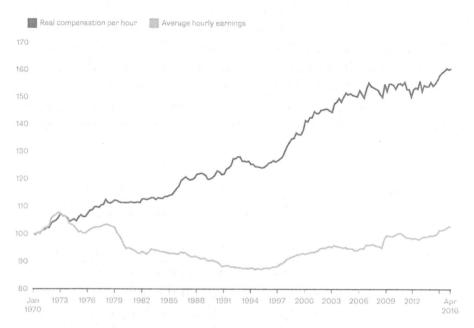

Figure 2. Compensation, including Benefits, Versus Take-HomePay. Includes benefits, indexed to 100, and adjusted for inflation. Source: Barry Ritholtz, "Health-Care Costs Ate Your Pay Raises," [16]

are $30,000 a year and the person is making $30,000, their total package could be $60,000, but they're not seeing it."[15]

A Sneak Attack

Imagine if a foreign country were causing this kind of collateral damage on our economy. We'd go to war in a second. Yet, we haven't. Evidence of the industry's "sneak attack" on the U.S. is clear. To wit…

Household income has been devastated by health care costs.

According to an article in the *Annals of Family Medicine*, from 2000 to 2009 the average annual increase in insurance premiums was 8 percent. During the same time frame, household incomes rose an average of 2.1 percent. If health insurance premiums and national wages continue to grow at these rates, the average cost of a family health insurance premium will equal 50 percent of all household income by 2021—and exceed 100 percent of household income by 2033.[17] This is at least partly to blame for the fact that *nearly seven in 10 Americans have less than $1,000 in savings.*[18]

Illness or medical bills contributed to 62 percent of all bankruptcies in 2007.

This is up from 46 percent in 2001.[19] In 2013, more than 1.5 million Americans lived in households that experienced a health-related bankruptcy. More than three-quarters of those people had insurance.[20] Some say medical bills may also be the top cause of homelessness. Nearly half of all GoFundMe crowdfunding campaigns are to pay for medical related expenses.[21]

State-level data demonstrate that health care is choking other budgets such as education.

Massachusetts is a cautionary tale. Its move to almost universal health care insurance in 2006 became the model for reform nationwide, the Affordable Care Act. While the state did see coverage increases, Figure 3 shows this came at a 37 percent increase in health care costs. As a result, funding in education decreased by 12.2 percent, mental health by 22.2 percent, and local aid by 50.5 percent. Frequently in education, what used to be paid for by taxes has been cut entirely and parents or teachers have to raise money to ensure their children get core school programs. In other words, we're stealing our kids' future.

Massachusetts was also forced to cut infrastructure spending, which dropped 14 percent. And Massachusetts is hardly alone. At both the state and federal level, trains are literally going off the tracks and bridges are falling into rivers as health care costs have starved budgets of infrastructure investment.

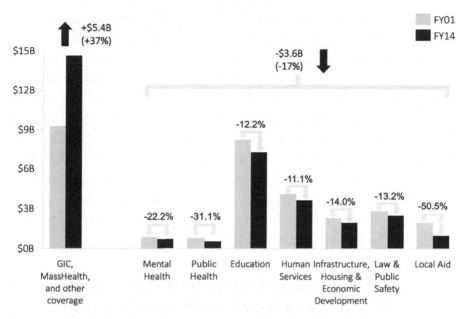

Figure 3. Source: Health Policy Commission, "List of Figures in 2013 Cost Trends Report by the Health Policy Commission." [22]

Between 2004 and 2014, officials in the little town of China, Maine, saw health insurance costs go up 141 percent to $200,000 per year for 11 municipal employees; the cost for just one of those employees with dependents equals the town's entire parks and recreation budget or the operating budget for one of its three volunteer fire departments. Instead of repaving roads, China is patching budgets. Beyond these microcosms, there are hundreds of millions of dollars in unfunded pension commitments around the country.[23]

More than 210,000 people die each year from preventable medical error in hospitals and other health care settings.[24]

It's the fifth leading cause of death in the U.S. after respiratory disease, accidents, stroke, and Alzheimer's.[25] Note that this is more than the number of soldiers killed in WWII.[26]

These deaths are primarily due to infections, along with errors in prescribing and administering drugs, mistaken diagnoses, botched surgeries and procedures, falls, and communication lapses from one care provider to another. The number of preventable adverse events associated with hospital care every day is 10,000—the medical equivalent of "friendly fire" happening seven times per minute. As with most cases of friendly fire, it's leadership and design that are most often at fault, rather than individuals. For detailed information on this subject, check out Sarah Kliff's powerful exposé on the flawed medical culture, "Do No Harm,"[27] and Dr. Marty Makary's book, *Unaccountable*,[28] which brings these statistics to life in devastating detail.

Hyperinflating health care costs have significantly reduced retirement savings.

I did some very rough, back-of-envelope calculations on what could be put into people's retirement plans if not for hyperinflating health care costs. I used historical rates of inflation, S&P growth, and health care premiums. Over 30 years, the average American household would have around $1,000,000 in their retirement account (assuming growth in an S&P index fund).[29] As things stand, the majority of Americans have next to no retirement savings and 68 percent of millennials aren't participating in a job-related retirement plan.[30]

There are unprecedented levels of dissatisfaction and burnout by doctors.

According to a Doctors Company survey of 5,000 physicians, 9 out of 10 physician respondents indicated an unwillingness to recommend health care as a profession.[31] A major reason is the layering of more and more bureaucracy. A recent study found that for every hour physicians see patients, they spend nearly two additional hours on recordkeeping.[32] Another reason is they're forced to see too many patients too fast, robbing them and patients of the ability to effectively diagnose or of any sense of connection or satisfaction.[33] Sadly, doctors have the highest rate of suicide of any profession.[34]

The High Cost of Poor Care

Dying is a good example of how we overspend on care we shouldn't be receiving in the first place. As renowned physician, policy analyst, and author Atul Gawande covered in his book *Being Mortal: Medicine and What Matters in the End*, the U.S. does a horrendous job dealing with end-of-life issues. This often leads, as Ken Murray, MD put it, to "misery we would not inflict on a terrorist" for our loved ones.[35] It also squanders billions of dollars. Approximately 30 percent of all Medicare spending is in the last six months of life, most of it unnecessary and much of it harmful.

Knowing the limits of medicine and what impacts quality of life, many doctors die differently than the rest of us, said Murray, meaning they die with much less intervention (and cost). People in La Crosse, Wisconsin, happily for them, are not like the rest of us: 96 percent of residents have advance directives saying how they wish to be treated at the end of life—and those wishes are respected. Now look at the cost differential: $18,000 for care in the last two years of life in La Crosse vs. a national average of $26,000. At one hospital in New York City, this is more than $75,000.[36]

Musculoskeletal (MSK) procedures, primarily surgeries such as knee replacements and spinal fusions, are another example of our overspending on care we don't want or need. The *Atlantic* reported in "When Evidence Says No, but Doctors Say Yes" how pervasive overtreatment is in areas such as stents and musculoskeletal procedures.[37] In fact, benefits expert Brian Klepper, formerly CEO of the National Alliance of Health Care Purchaser Coalitions, estimates that 2 percent of the entire U.S. economy (not just health care) is wasted on non-evidence-based MSK procedures that add no value. How can that be? Health care spending is nearly 20 percent of the national economy, MSK procedures are typically 20 percent of healthcare spending, and only 50 percent of MSK procedures are evidence-based.[38]

Health care is a $3 trillion dollar industry and 30 cents of every one of those dollars spent on health care is wasted, according to the Institute of Medicine. In 2009, that was $750 billion. Imagine what we could do with that money.[39]

- Send every 17- and 18-year-old to a state university for four years
- Fund the Department of Defense for a year
- Cover all hospital and medical care for veterans for 51 years
- Pay for all U.S. economic aid to foreign countries for 36 years (and still have $14 billion left over)
- Cover all annual health care costs for the uninsured six times over

Yet, despite all this waste and devastation, and despite employers spending huge sums to keep up with hyperinflating costs, the reality is status quo health benefits are a horrible value proposition for employers and individuals.

For example, flawed reimbursement incentives have made primary care a "loss leader," like milk in the back of the grocery store (i.e., a low-margin item designed to get customers to purchase high margin items). The result is rushed appointments, unnecessary referrals to specialty care, and lower pay, making the discipline increasingly unappealing to physicians. Unsurprisingly, this has led to a primary care shortage. This leads to long wait times to see a primary care physician or no access at all, which can cause small health care fires to become 5-alarm medical infernos. In short, undervaluing primary care is the root cause of medically unnecessary office appointments, clogged waiting rooms, and unconscionable delays in care for people who truly need a face-to-face encounter.

Not surprisingly, Figure 4 shows that Net Promoter Scores, a common measure of customer satisfaction, shows the health insurance industry is lower than even cable companies.

Health Insurance: Lowest Customer Satisfaction of Any Industry

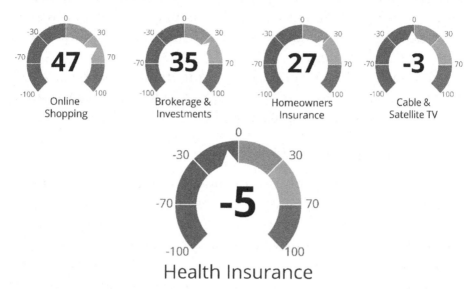

Figure 4. *Note that some industries have so many detractors that the score becomes negative.*[40]

A Way Out

While the status quo "preservatives" squabble in DC, forward-leaning individuals and organizations aren't waiting around. They see the threat for what it is and are creating examples for all of us to follow. There is a budding partnership between clinicians dissatisfied with the status quo, citizens who realize they have more power than they'd imagined, and employers no longer willing to passively accept further theft of the American dream.

Jeffrey Brenner, MD—executive director of The Camden Coalition of Health Care Providers and MacArthur Genius Award winner for his work using data to identify and improve the care of high-cost, high-need patients—put it succinctly in a *Freakonomics* interview: "There comes a point in a democracy when the public's had enough and they stand up."[41] For many across all segments of health care and all political persuasions, that time is now.

The three most trusted professions in the U.S. are nurses, doctors, and pharmacists. A key reason I love working in the health care industry is the great people I've gotten to know. However, great people inside a flawed system will always underperform those in a great system.

While it will take clinicians and others of all stripes to lead the movement, doctors have a unique role to play. In fact, some doctors are leading the revolution. Here are just two examples.

Rushika Fernandopulle, MD

Rushika is a practicing physician and cofounder and CEO of Iora Health, a health care services firm based in Boston. He was also the first executive director of the Harvard Interfaculty Program for Health Systems Improvement, and managing director of the Clinical Initiatives Center at the Advisory Board Company. Fernandopulle was among the first to understand that caring for the care team is foundational to achieving the best outcomes and reducing unnecessary costs and treatment. His work was featured in The New Yorker article "Hot Spotters," which highlighted the best ways to care for the sickest patients in our cities.[42]

Iora's mission is to build a radically new primary care model that improves quality and service, while reducing overall costs. It has opened successful practices in a wide variety of clinic settings, serving casino union workers, university employees, freelancers, undocumented workers, and Medicare recipients.

Rajaie Batniji, MD

Rajaie and his cofounder Ali Diab started Collective Health to help employees receive better care and coverage than the typical health plan. To tackle this challenge, they pulled together a team that could come at it from all angles—design, engineering, finance, law, medicine, product development, and operations. What they came up with is a smarter, more flexible alternative that connects a company's medical, pharmaceutical, dental, and vision plans on a single platform.

The impetus for Collective Health was Diab's horrible experience battling an insurance company that did not want to pay his massive medical bills following emergency abdominal surgery. The insurer claimed some of his surgical and hospital charges were experimental or the result of physician error, leaving Diab holding the bag for a shockingly large portion of the bill.

As a physician and political economist, Batniji had seen this scenario play out many times before: individuals left to advocate for themselves in a system where all of the economic incentives are misaligned and where getting answers about costs is impossible. Enter Collective Health, which was designed specifically for self-insured employers, two-thirds of the employer-provided health care market.

For these health care revolutionaries, it's what Ronald Reagan called Morning in America.

Rosie the Restorer

In family discussions about the need to fix health care, I explained to my son how every now and then the country is able to really pull together. I used Rosie the Riveter as a symbol from WWII. We decided we needed a new symbol of someone who was truly heroic and could get the job—any job—done. My son knew instantly who it should be: mom! Rosie the Restorer here is a mashup of a superhero, a mom, and Rosie the Riveter. [Courtesy of Cameron Chase, age 12]

PITTSBURGH (ALLEGHENY COUNTY) SCHOOLS

Bucking old habits that are devastating education funding elsewhere, forward-looking teacher union and school board leaders in Allegheny County, Pennsylvania are proving that it's not really so difficult to slay the health care cost beast and save their kids' future—even in an expensive and contentious health care market. Understandably, unions want their members to be fairly compensated and keep schools from being decimated. Recognizing that they share the same goals, the school board decided to take a new approach.

Assuming the current trend continues, kindergartners entering Pittsburgh area schools will collectively have $2 billion more available to invest in education and services over the course of their school years than their counterparts across the state in Philadelphia. In Philadelphia, schools pay $8,815 per member for teacher health benefits. The Allegheny County Schools Health Insurance Consortium (ACSHIC), with 48,000 covered lives, pays $4,661 per member—$199 million less per year. Class sizes in Pittsburgh are 30 percent smaller, teachers are paid better with better benefits, and there are four times as many librarians.

Rewarding Wise Decisions

Jan Klein, ACSHIC's business manager, describes a model that is very consistent with the Health Rosetta blueprint. In a nutshell, they make smart decisions free or nearly free (e.g., primary care is free and going to high-quality care providers involves very low or no copays or deductibles) and poor decisions expensive (e.g., pay more to see higher cost, lower quality care providers). It's a much more subtle, yet more effective, strategy than blunt-instrument, high-deductible plans that often lead to deferred care, bankruptcies, reduced teacher compensation, fewer arts programs… the list goes on.

The consortium is managed by 24 trustees, equal parts labor and management. When consultants attend consortium meetings, they often can't tell who is who. Many times, union leaders are more aggressive in pushing forward new initiatives. While other employers have blithely accepted 5 to 20 percent annual health care cost increases, the consortium spent $233 million in annual claims in 2016—*down* from $241 million in 2014. The consortium is able to manage their costs without any stop loss insurance because they have control over what they call their benefit grid, a program that was defined and embraced by both union leaders and teachers.

They've accomplished this despite the fact that care provider organization consolidation in Western Pennsylvania has reduced competition and raised health care costs with little to no improvement in quality of care—and despite an ongoing war between the largest hospital, the University of Pittsburgh Medical Center (UPMC), and the largest local insurance carrier, Highmark.

Understanding that the best way to spend less is to improve health care quality, ACSHIC found that the path began with the following steps.

- Educating consortium trustees on quality rankings of hospitals, including sending them to a Pittsburgh Business Group on Health forum

- Retrieving hospital quality data through third-party data and tools (e.g., Imagine Health, CareChex, and Innovu)
- Validating vendor information by confirming it was not influenced by bias
- Selecting the most effective resources by identifying credible partners/vendors

Once educated, the trustees provided the following direction to the team developing the new school district health plan.

- Use quality measures from respected third-party sources
- Create tiered products so people are free to go wherever they want for care—but they pay more if they choose sites that have lower quality and value
- Focus on ease of access to regional clinics and hospitals
- Focus on the relationship between cost and quality (the former turned out not to be indicative of the latter)
- Educate members, especially about why the local academic medical center was placed in a high-cost tier (it wasn't the highest-quality facility for many kinds of care)
- Address member concerns (e.g., will this really save money?) through continuous communication

Spending Before Changes
(October 2013 - September 2014)

# 1 Hospital in the region	#32 Hospital in the region
(highest-quality rating)	*(low-quality rating)*
33,352 Services*	31,047 Services*
293 Admits	362 Admits
$4,941,146 total	$15,089,972 total

Total spend: $20,031,118

Services include imaging, lab test, outpatient procedures, etc.

To improve value, ACSHIC implemented tiered benefit offerings tied to high-quality care providers.

- Enhanced tier has NO deductible and pays 100 percent of hospital charges
- Standard tier has a deductible and pays 80 percent of hospital charges
- Out-of-network care has a larger deductible and pays 50 percent of hospital charges
- Lower cost and higher quality is determined by independent third-party, benchmarks

Spending After Changes
(October 2015 - September 2016)

 # 1 Hospital in the region　　　　**#32 Hospital in the region**

(highest-quality rating)　　　　　　*(low-quality rating)*

40,046 Services* (+20%)　　　　6,620 Services* (-79%)
328 Admits (+12%)　　　　　　113 Admits (-69%)
$7,120,357 total (+44%)　　　　$5,548,832 total (-63%)

Total spend: $12,669,189 (-36.8%)

In sum, the consortium reduced hospital spending by $7.36 million, a 36.8% reduction

*Services include imaging, lab test, outpatient procedures, etc.

Going Forward

The consortium expects to continue enhancing benefits with only a very modest premium increase of 1.9 percent for members. Here are a few plan attributes going forward.

- The enhanced tier has no deductibles
- Primary care visits have no copay
- Specialist visits have a $10 copay
- An employee assistance program provider
- A second opinion service

Their determination to serve kids led education leaders in Pittsburgh to move past tired assumptions about labor and management being forever at odds over health benefits. With any luck, their steely resolve in the face of local challenges will inspire teachers' unions and school boards throughout the country to say NO to health care stealing our kids' future.

CHAPTER 2

HEALTH CARE PRICES: HYPERINFLATION OR FLAT?

Jeanne Pinder

A curious thing has happened in health care pricing in this country. While insurance premiums and prices for common procedures for insured people go up and up and up, cash or negotiated self-pay prices* for many procedures vary little from year to year.

But wait, I can hear you saying, health care prices always go up, don't they? They do if they go through a PPO or major insurance carrier. But for the most part, negotiated cash or self-pay prices don't, at least not consistently. Sometimes they modestly increase, but more often they stay the same—or even go down from year to year. Our team of journalists noticed this pattern when we began comparing data sets year over year from the same locations.

We have been surveying care providers about their cash or self-pay prices for five years and have a very good set of data for 13 metro areas. Some did, indeed, raise rates regularly, but they tended to be the higher-priced care providers in the first place. Overall the flatline pattern is clear.

---

* *For the purposes of this book, a "cash price" is what a provider charges an individual who is either paying directly, using a check or credit card, or is covered by an employer or union that pays immediately under a direct contract that bypasses the insurance claims processing process.*

For example, we recently re-reported our New York City cash prices. The following figures show the trend for MRIs and ultrasounds. Note the wild variation in pricing among care providers, which persists across regions, cities, and even within individual health care systems and hospitals. This reflects yet another health care cost problem: unpredictability and variability of cost for the same procedures.*

Procedure: Pelvic Ultrasound

Facility	Code	2011	2012	2013	2017
Dynamic Medical Imaging	76856	X	$125	$125	$125
Neighborhood Radiology	76856	X	X	$150	$132
New Millennium Medical	76856	X	$150	$150	$150
Hudson Valley Radiological Associates	76856	$198	$198	$213	$158
Rochester General Hospital	76856	X	X	$229	$212
Greenwich Radiology Group	76856	X	X	$344	$344
Brooklyn Heights Imaging	76856	X	$185	$185	$375
Highway Imaging Associates	76856	X	$175	$175	$375
Diagnostic Imaging of Millford	76856	X	X	$314	$413
East River Medical Imaging	76856	X	$377	$377	$754
Lawrence Hospital	76856	X	X	$654	$792
Crescent Radiology	76856	$150	$150	X	X
Diagnostic Imaging Services Bronxville	76856	$469	$491	X	X
Empire Imaging	76856	$175	$200	X	X
Manhasset Diagnostic	76856	$300	$85	X	X
New York Imagery	76856	$350	$207	X	X
New York Westchester Square Med. Center	76856	$648	$700	X	X
Park Avenue Radiologists	76856	$366	$325	X	X

---

* *It's worth noting that overall hyperinflation in health care spending is multivariate. It comes partially from the issues discussed here. Another major source is care and procedures that shouldn't happen at all, as a result of overuse, misdiagnosis, unnecessary, or ineffective treatment and procedures. We discuss this separate, but related, issue in Chapter 12.*

Procedure: Lower back MRI without contrast

Facility	Code	2011	2012	2013	2017
Advanced Radiology	72148	$1,160	$1,160	$1,093	$0
Queens Radiology/Olympic Open MRI	72148	$400	$450	$450	$0
Neighborhood Radiology	72148	X	$150	$150	$150
Radiology of Westchester	72148	X	X	$450	$450
Middle Village Radiology	72148	$350	$450	$450	$500
New Rochelle Radiology	72148	X	X	$500	$500
Greater Waterbury Imaging Center	72148	X	$185	$185	$375
Housatonic Valley Radiology Assoc.	72148	X	X	$816	$627
East River Medical Imaging	72148	$1,900	$1,900	$1,200	$1,900
Columbus Circle Imaging	72148	X	X	$1,200	$2,600
East Manhattan Diagnostic Imaging	72148	X	X	$1,200	$2,600
Union Square Diagnostic Imaging	72148	$800	$1,800	$1,200	$2,600
Advanced Radiology	72148	$1,064	$556	X	X
Astoria Medical Imaging	72148	$450	$1,200	X	X
Park Avenue Radiologists	72148	$1,000	$0	X	X

Source: ClearHealthCosts. Used with Permission.[43]

Unpredictable Costs

Premiums go up, deductibles go up, out-of-pocket spending goes up, as Figure 5 shows. Inexorably, inevitably. Or so we are told.

But if you look deeper, pricing and costs are completely unpredictable.

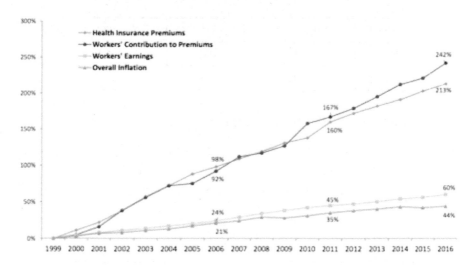

Figure 5. Cumulative Increases in Health Insurance Premiums, General Annual Deductibles, Inflation, and Workers' Earnings, 2011-2016. Source: Employer Health Benefit Survey 2016, Kaiser Family Foundation and Health Research & Education Trust.[44]

Below is a sample of comparative prices graciously given to us a couple of years ago by a care provider organization. The table below shows charged rates, reimbursement rates, and individual responsibility for a selected group of procedures at the organization. Each row is for a different individual on a different health plan.

As you can see, if you have a $10,000 deductible, you might exhaust that deductible before you get to anything else, depending on the "insurance paid" or "negotiated" rate. Or, you might spend only $2,681 towards your deductible.

Example 1: Knee arthroscopy

Charges range from $13,452 to $19,187
Insurance payments range from $2,681 to $13,607
508% variation in the actual paid amount

CPT Code	Billed, Cash or Self-Pay Price	Insurance Paid Amt.	Patient Responsibility
29881	$15,233.58	$2,681.36	$350

29881	$19,187.85	$3,795.20	$948.80
29881	$13,452.86	$9,080.77	$1,008.91
29881	$18,142.68	$13,607	$0

Example 2: Repair Initial inguinal hernia (No. 1 and No. 2)

Charges range from $13,950 to $22,184
Payments range from $2,515 to $12,281
500% variation in the actual paid amount

Figure #1

CPT Code	Billed, Cash or Self-Pay Price	Insurance Paid Amt.	Patient Responsibility
36561	$13,950.29	$2,514.75	$641.52
36561	$15,680.49	$8,467.46	$940.83
36561	$15,948.16	$11,961.10	$0

Figure #2

CPT Code	Billed, Cash or Self-Pay Price	Insurance Paid Amt.	Patient Responsibility
49505	$22,183.85	$3,008.58	$767.50
49505	$17,011.54	$4,576	$1,144
49505	$18,193.78	$12,280.80	$1,364.53

Example 3: Carpal tunnel surgery

Charges range from $9,694 to $11,721
Payments range from $1,953 to $7,079
362% variation in the actual paid amount

CPT Code	Billed, Cash or Self-Pay Price	Insurance Paid Amt.	Patient Responsibility
64721	$9,694.24	$1,953.47	$0

64721	$11,106.59	$3,174.30	$452.70
64721	$11,721.45	$3,501	$0
64721	$10,097.93	$7,079.25	$494.20

Example 4: Cataract surgery with intraocular lens (IOL)

Charges from $10,456 to $12,831
Insurance payments range from $2,474 to $8,024
324% variation in the actual paid amount

CPT Code	Billed, Cash or Self-Pay Price	Insurance Paid Amt.	Patient Responsibility
66984	$10,456.39	$2,473.63	$0
66984	$12,831.26	$2,473.63	$0
66984	$10,878.50	$2,473.63	$0
66984	$10,606.54	$4,328	$100
66984	$11,503.16	$8,024.07	$603.30

Source: ClearHealthCosts. Used with permission.[45]

If you're not surprised and shocked yet, get ready. Insured individuals who ask for cash prices pay less than other insured individuals. For example, in San Francisco, Castro Valley Open MRI charges $475 cash for a lower back MRI. An insured individual who asked for a cash price for the same MRI at a different care provider knocked a $1,850 bill down to $580. A different insured individual was initially charged $5,667 for the same MRI at a third care provider. Their insurer paid $2,367 and the individual was asked to pay $1,114.54, a total of $3,471.54 to the third care provider for the same $475 MRI. It's enough to make your head spin.

However, there's a trend toward transparency for competitive and regulatory reasons. Fore example, Surgery Center of Oklahoma founder, Keith Smith, MD, has been publicizing cash prices online for nearly nine years.

"I've only changed them four times," he said. "And in every case, I lowered them. So I think I could make a compelling case that prices are actually falling."

Smith is still making money too, he said, often paying doctors more for procedures than insurers. "If we realize some efficiency in our practice that we've not seen before, then our inclination is to pass that savings along to the buyer and make ourselves even more competitive in the market."

More and more providers are following his practice of posting cash prices publicly, pushing us closer to the day when anyone can walk into a facility or physician's office with a price and insist they step up and match it.

Third Parties, Intermediaries, and Escalator Clauses

So what causes insurance premiums and noncash prices to continue going up?

For one thing, contracts between providers and payers can include things like automatic escalator clauses, which stipulate that payment rates automatically increase each year.

Then there's the chargemaster, the list of prices at a hospital or other health care provider. Here's how one hospital executive explained the chargemaster to me: "Bob in accounting made that list in the 1960s, and we just raise prices every year. But don't tell anybody—we like them to think it's because our cost of business keeps going up, and because of uncompensated care, and because of the burden of keeping an ER open 24-7, and because health care is just expensive."

And then there are all the people behind the scenes between you and your doctor, each taking a dime or a dollar or a hundred dollars out of every transaction. For example, a good size hospital probably has multiple vice-presidents for strategic planning, armies of business-office workers, pricing consultants, and people to make revenue-cycle management projections—just as the insurance company does.

There are a lot of people in corporate medicine who make a ton of money off the lack of market-competitive pricing, Smith said. And these people don't want to give that game up. But Smith says it's a myth that insurance companies care about prices.

"They really don't. All they care about are charges, because they're in the business of selling discounts. The higher the prices are to start with, the more money they make in discounting those prices. So that's part of the problem; a PPO will say that their discount saved an employer tens of thousands of dollars—in which they naturally share."

Turning Things Around

Joining Smith in his cynicism is Mike Dendy, who predicts the PPO concept will die out over the next few years.

Dendy is CEO of Advanced Medical Pricing Solutions, a Georgia-based company that does health cost management for self-insured employer health plans. They help employers beat back costs using tools like close scrutiny of bills, the formation of narrower networks, direct contracting between providers and employers, and reference-based pricing services, often based on Medicare reimbursement rates. Dendy said providers commonly charge 300 to 500 percent of Medicare's rate and even the largest employers pay 250 percent on average, including both in- and out-of-network claims, although he's seen hospitals creep up to 700 percent.

"The last report I saw showed the average spending by an employer group last year was about $18,300 per employee," he said.

"It's getting unsustainable—and every 4 or 5 percent increase now is a lot bigger than it was 20 years ago. The situation can be remedied, but you need consumerism to make it happen: incentives or disincentives for the consumer. And then you need technology and information immediately available, so people can make the correct decision in non-emergency situations."

Dendy further predicted that the insurance market will move

toward defined contribution plans, where an employer's spending would be limited in scope. He compared employer health policies with travel policies. If you're traveling for the company, he said, the company limits your outlay.

"Nobody thinks they're being grossly burdened by not being able to stay at the Four Seasons and eat steak five times a day (unless they're paying for it themselves). But under current health insurance arrangements, via a PPO, an employee is free to choose an expensive MRI or an expensive hospital—and that raises everybody's premiums," he said.

Jeanne Pinder is founder and CEO of ClearHealthCosts, an independent health care research organization; its team of independent journalists is dedicated to finding and publishing costs for medical procedures and items.

CHAPTER 3

WHAT YOU DON'T KNOW ABOUT THE PRESSURES AND CONSTRAINTS FACING INSURANCE EXECUTIVES COSTS YOU DEARLY

For all the recent talk about accountable care organizations, there is a distinct lack of accountability when it comes to health care costs. Hospitals blame insurance companies, insurance companies blame hospitals, providers blame the government, and everyone blames drug companies. Even though many employers have woken up to the fact that they can get better bang for their buck if they are self-insured, most self-insured employers still don't pay close attention to the critical details that often have the most dramatic impact on their bottom line.

Here's why: Virtually every conversation I have with employers reveals a profound lack of understanding of market dynamics, constraints, and incentives that health insurance company executives face. For the most part, these executives are good people operating perfectly rationally, given the drivers and constraints of their business.. These constraints include care provider organization practices, Wall Street profit expectations, employer demands (yes, you!), individual employee behavior, and regulatory issues. Unfortunately, the net result incentivizes redistributing profits from companies like yours to the health care industry. In short, their incentives are not aligned with yours. Like hospitals (the biggest recipient of your health care dollars), insurance companies win when health care costs go up.

Understanding the specific pressures facing insurance company executives will help you more effectively negotiate and drive better value from your health dollars. Plus, several of these pressures are a direct byproduct of employer behavior you can do something about.

The items below came directly from seasoned executives in national and regional health insurance companies. They asked for anonymity, as they are either still working in these organizations or don't want to face market blowback.

Pressure to Include Less Desirable Hospitals in Networks

This is caused by pressure from employers to have every possible provider in their network so their employees don't complain about lack of choice. Of course, having every provider means that you have lower- and higher-quality providers in the same network. This also means higher costs because the lower-quality providers are generally less efficient and deliver improper, excessive, or low-value care, which leads to complications and overtreatment.

In addition, contracts between insurance carriers and hospitals in some regions include anti-steerage language. This language requires the insurer to include a given health system network in all of its plans. For example, in northern California, UnitedHealthcare might have an agreement with Sutter Health that prevents them from excluding Sutter from any employer agreement. Or in Dallas, Texas Health Resources might demand the same thing of Blue Cross. The Affordable Care Act (ACA) made this worse by allowing hospitals to aggregate in ways that enable oligopolistic practices.

Plus, employers often seek to include their local hospital and every physician in-network to minimize employee complaints, regardless of the hospital's or physician's quality (or cost).

Poor Service from Carriers Is a Natural Byproduct of Medical Loss Ratio Rules

This is a direct effect of the ACA. Because the Medical Loss Ratio prescribed in the ACA requires that 80 or 85 percent of premiums be spent on medical care (depending on type of plan), carriers are forced to cut customer service employees for fully-insured plans—considered overhead—to escape penalties under the ACA. This is exacerbated as companies move from fully-insured to self-insured status (in part to escape ACA regulations). Because customer service functions are often shared across fully-insured and self-insured business, the lower-margin self-insured business puts further pressure on carriers to find cost savings. Generally, self-insured plans have less than 10 percent the profit opportunity of fully-insured plans.[46]

In addition, Medical Loss Ratio requirements cap insurance company profits, meaning that the only practical ways to increase revenue (and thus profits) is to reduce service staff, raise premiums, or process more claims. The carriers have no choice but to tighten their expenses to still make profit margins, even paring back on high-cost executives.

This dynamic parallels what I observed in the shift from high-margin mainframes and minicomputers from IBM, DEC, Wang, Data General and others to low-margin PC manufacturers. At a time when there was a dramatic need for reinvention and innovative new offerings, those organizations lost most of their best (and most marketable) leaders, leaving them with the risk averse, mediocre performers. The result for most was a death spiral—IBM being the exception because of the leadership of Lou Gerstner. Unsustainable cost structures and weakened management devastate incumbents in times of great change, whether you are a minicomputer maker or health insurer.

New Fees to Replace Lost Margin

The co-dependent relationship between insurance carriers and hospitals is evident with out-of-network charges. Remember, when health systems impose egregious out-of-network charges, insurers are happy to pay them immediately and with no review whatsoever (and with your money), because it generates more revenue for them in a number of ways. Naturally, they can't say this. Plus, employers have been haranguing them for decades any time an employee complains about any delayed or denied claim, or balance bill from a care provider. So in response to this profit incentive and an attempt to give you what your benefits managers ask for, they sell this as a benefit for you: You and your employees won't be bothered by hospital collections departments!

They follow this up with "re-pricing" that discounts charges to seemingly more reasonable levels—on your behalf, of course. What may not be clear is that the insurance carrier gets paid a share of the repriced claim. This encourages the hospital to push the pre-discount prices ever higher, which pushes the discount up and, with it, the fee paid by the employer and net amount of each claim.

Another fee opportunity is so-called "pay and chase" programs, in which the insurance carrier doing your claims administration gets paid 30-40 percent for recovering fraudulent or duplicative claims. Thus, there is a perverse incentive to tacitly allow fraudulent and duplicative claims to be paid, get paid as the plan administrator, then get paid a second time for recovering the originally paid claim.

Many of the fraud prevention tools used by claims administrators are laughably outdated and weak compared to what they are up against. Modern payment integrity solutions can stop fraud and duplicate claims, but aren't being used by most self-insured companies' claims administrators. In a report on fraud, Accenture found, "Estimates by government and law enforcement agencies such as the FBI place the loss due to health care fraud as high as 10 percent of annual health care expenditure."[47] This is roughly $300 billion per year! Payment integrity experts, such as Dave Adams, CEO of 4C Health Solutions, tell me stories of companies that have paid the same claim 25-50 times because the claims administrator didn't use modern tools to stop it. Many times they don't do anything about it. Other times they do a bill review and try to recover those monies, getting the "pay and chase" recovery payment.

It's worth noting again that employee behavior is often a primary root cause of these practices. Whenever employees get a bill from a care provider as a result of a denied claim, they complain to your HR department or broker, who in turn complains to the insurance carrier, leading them to give your company what you ask for. As with most dysfunction in health care, simple incentives and behaviors often have enormous, counterintuitive, and costly consequences.

Dancing the Frustrating Kabuki Dance

Why does an insurance carrier give you a renewal rate and then keep reducing it until you bite, especially when you're fully-insured? Because the insurance carrier makes ten times more on premiums from fully-insured clients than on fees from self-insured clients.[48] Because of this, insurance executives face enormous pressure to keep and grow their fully-insured books of business. Bonuses and other incentives for benefits brokers and consultants to keep business with the same carrier cement this dynamic. Increasingly, carriers even offer early renewals to keep fully-insured business. Often these early renewals come with no-shop clauses. So, a 20 percent rate increase may only be 15 percent if you sign today and agree not to shop the competition.

This should be viewed as a red-flag, not a great deal on a premium reduction. The first thing to do if you ever get a no-shop offer is to warm up the RFPs and start shopping.

Your Claims Data Somehow Belongs to the Insurance Carrier

Amazingly, insurance carriers have convinced employers to accept that their own claims data are proprietary to the carrier—and they refuse to share them. Equally amazingly, employers often agree to contract terms that severely limit their access to audit claims, often being able to audit just a tiny subset.

There are only three reasons insurance carriers would say the data is proprietary.

1. Their reporting and data systems are so poor that they literally can't share. This is much less likely these days.
2. If they release the data, a good actuary consultant could dive in and raise lots of questions they don't want to answer. For example, they could see that an organization pays a large multiple of market pricing or has questionably high use of a particular test or procedure.
3. They want to maintain the status quo. This means protecting pricing opacity at all costs. If you could see the prices you actually pay, you might begin to wonder why a hospital with a large market share but mediocre quality outcomes is paid exponentially more than a smaller, high-quality provider in the same network.

It should be clear that numbers two and three are more likely. Hospitals and insurance carriers want to avoid defending or explaining pricing and the various fees they bake in. This largely comes from the pressure insurance and hospital executives face to keep growing profits by 10 to 15 percent year over year.

Inflated Health Care Cost Trends

Insurance executives are under huge pressure to grow their business, even if it is self-insured accounts. One way insurance carriers try to prevent independent third-party plan administrators from winning employer business is inflating the medical trend (the rate at which health care costs are increasing) for their fully-insured clients by 1 percent. This additional money is then used to create bonuses (override programs) for benefits brokers, workplace wellness programs, and broker implementation credits (additional payments for help rolling out a program). These incentives further help win or maintain fully-insured and self-insured clients. Think of this as robbing Peter, unknowingly, to pay Paul. As a result, fully-insured clients are cross-subsidizing low-value workplace wellness programs or paying to fund broker override programs that do not impact them at all.

Broker Incentives that Preserve Status Quo Inertia

Insurance carriers often have programs that require a broker to maintain a 90 percent retention rate to receive a year-end bonus. These programs help carriers retain clients and can be $300,000 to $500,000 for each local office of a brokerage. This amount often represents most of the net profit for an office and can heavily influence brokers who might otherwise advise you to move to a self-insured plan. Because bonuses are based on the total business a particular broker brings to an insurance carrier, they typically aren't included in the list of claims costs, commissions, or fees, unless the broker has a transparent practice—which most don't.

If it seems like your broker makes your current carrier's renewal plan look better than other options, this is probably why. You might want to ask if he or she gets paid any bonuses from particular carriers. To simplify this, Appendix C has a disclosure form you can use to understand your broker's overall financial incentives and potential conflicts before making a purchasing decision.[49]

In short, the broker you treat as your buyer's agent is actually compensated as a seller's agent, creating a conflict you wouldn't accept in other contexts.

Carriers and Brokers Are
Soft on Area Hospitals

When your insurance carrier also administers the health plan for hospital employees or your broker represents the hospital, there are additional forces working against you. Hospitals are often one of the larger employers in a town or region, so the insurance carrier won't risk losing them as a client. Since the hospital provides a large revenue stream, the carrier typically goes easy on them when negotiating pricing on behalf of other clients—like you. Additionally, some brokers get as much as 30 percent of their revenue from hospitals and other care providers. You should always ask your benefits broker or claims administrator if a local hospital is a client, as that is a clear conflict-of-interest, especially when the hospital itself owns the insurance carrier.

State Mandates

One benefit of self-insuring is avoiding state mandates and regulatory requirements that apply to fully-insured plans and that can meaningfully increase your overall costs. This benefit disappears if your insurance carrier incorporates these into their self-insured plan offerings. Why would they do that? Different treatment of different business lines and employer accounts creates complexity that insurance carriers want to avoid. Logical and efficient for them. Costly for you.

CHAPTER 4

MILLENNIALS WILL REVOLUTIONIZE HEALTH BENEFITS

Boomers blamed their parents' generation for handing them a society rife with corruption and mindless conformity. Now it's their kids' turn to point the finger. Boomers are bankrupting the country in the name of health care that doesn't deliver on the quality or economic promises they bought hook, line, and sinker.

If we can't slay the health care beast, millennials will see their future stolen from them. As the largest generation in history and now the largest chunk of the workforce (see Figure 6), they will make their presence felt.

In millions

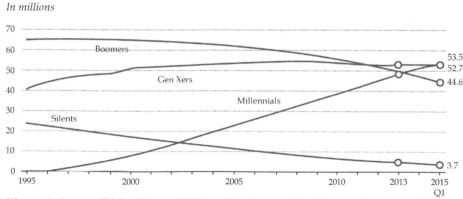

Figure 6. Source: Richard Fry, "Millennials Surpass Gen Xers as the Largest Genera-tion in U.S. Labor Force," Pew Research Center, (July 4th, 2016).[50]

47

Whether through government favoring the largest special interest groups (e.g., hospitals, pharmaceutical companies, and insurance companies) rather than the people or self-inflicted mistakes (e.g., the HMO "gatekeeper" and denial of care debacle), health care has been remarkably resilient to forces trying to disrupt it for decades—forces that have driven change in virtually every other sector from financial services to retail to travel. Millennials will bring this disruption to health care.

Becky and Her Biggest Expense

If you only read one (other) book about health care, read David Goldhill's *Catastrophic Care: Why Everything We Think We Know about Health Care Is Wrong*. Formerly CFO of a large media organization, Goldhill is currently CEO of The Game Show Network. He also lost his father to a hospital-acquired infection and saw numerous errors during that hospitalization. This experience caused Goldhill to bring his financial acumen to health care.

If he didn't break it down with well-sourced figures, Goldhill's conclusions would be unbelievable. Who could imagine that during their adult lives, one out of every two dollars earned by millennials over their careers will go to a health care system that is the perfect polar opposite to what they want and value? That is, if the current trajectory isn't altered. Keep in mind that, while well over 80 percent of health-related spending goes to the "sick care" system, that system only drives 20 percent of health outcomes.

Figure 7 tells a terrifying story, but more shocking is how conservative the assumptions behind the numbers are. The following description of these assumptions is from Goldhill's book.

Let's make a few assumptions about Becky's life. We'll say she gets married at thirty and has two children. She works until she's 65 and dies at 80. We'll also assume her income grows every year by 4 percent, so that at retirement she's earning $180,000 a year. To simplify the analysis, we'll have

Share of Lifetime Earnings of a Millennial That Will Go to Health Care Unless We Change Course

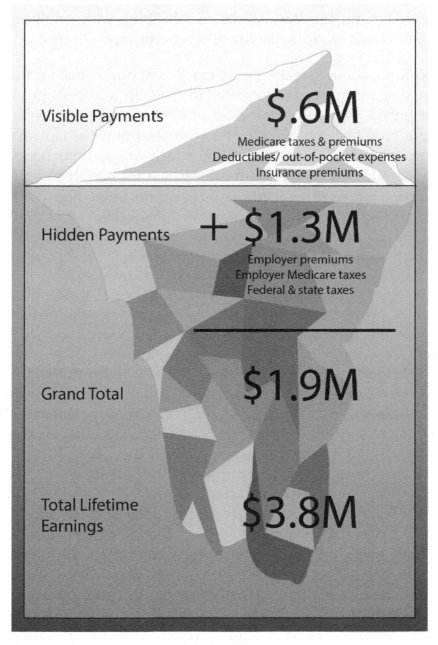

Figure 7. Source: Numbers come from Goldhill's book and are over the course of a millennial's lifetime.[51]

Becky's husband leave her to join an ashram when he turns 65, so she's only responsible for her own Medicare premiums. Let's also give Becky a stroke of good fortune and say that she and her dependents stay healthy, with no major health crisis requiring large out-of-pocket expenditures.

Now allow me to make a truly crazy assumption just for the sake of argument. Let's assume that health care costs grow at only 2 percent a year—half of Becky's income growth. This hasn't been true for forty-five years, but we can always hope. Given all those factors, how much do you think Becky will contribute to the health care system for herself and her dependents over her lifetime? I'll give you a hint: Becky will earn $3.85 million over her career. The answer is $1.9 million! If she has a working spouse, the two will contribute $2.5 million into this system over their lifetimes.[52]

How has this happened? Remember that Becky is almost certainly unaware of how many ways she is paying into the health care system, even though she'll probably put more into that system than she spends on anything else over her entire life.

This projection takes on added urgency when you consider that obesity rates have tripled among young adults in the past three decades, from 8 percent in 1971-1974 to 24 percent in 2005-2006, thanks to the diet of what Michael Pollan calls "food-like substances" that their Boomer parents fed them. This is causing millennials to engage more broadly in the health care system much earlier than previous generations. As Figure 8 shows, only 20 percent of health outcomes are the result of clinical care. The areas that represent the other 80 percent are a good place to start for understanding where millennials will likely take our health care system.

Finally, the jig is up. A do-it-yourself health reform movement is rising—and not a moment too soon. Solutions are coming from the edges: from forward-looking employers, innovative towns, fed-up physicians, and, especially, from millennials wising up. Ask any venture capitalist whom they study to get insight into the future and they'll give you a clear answer—millennials.

20%
CLINICAL CARE

ACCESS   QUALITY
TO CARE   OF CARE

30%
HEALTH BEHAVIORS

GENETICS   DIET &   TOBACCO   ALCOHOL &   SLEEP &   ACTIVITY
        EXERCISE   USE   DRUG USE   SEXUAL

EDUCATION   EMPLOYMENT   INCOME   FAMILY/   COMMUNITY
                          SOCIAL   SAFETY
                          SUPPORT

SOCIAL & ECONOMIC FACTORS
40%

AIR   WATER   HOUSING   TRANSIT
QUALITY   QUALITY

PHYSICAL ENVIRONMENT
10%

Figure 8. In the future, the health ecosystem will focus on the true drivers of outcomes, of which clinical care is only 20 percent. [53]

Millennials to the Rescue

Millennials, people currently 20-36 in 2017, have driven society-wide change in many areas. Their early adoption of technology made smartphones, social media, and services such as Uber pervasive across all generations. That row of empty storefronts in your town? That's the power of millennials.

Financial services is a good example of millennials steering the market away from today's market leaders.[54]

Well-known brand strategist Adam Hanft, author of *The Stunning Evolution of Millennials: They've Become the Ben Franklin Generation*, could have been talking about health care when he wrote:

[Millennials'] faith in technology is understandable. Algorithms don't act in their own self-interest. Algorithms weren't responsible for dreaming up sub-prime loans and nearly bringing down the financial system. Millennials didn't trust authority and conventional sources of wisdom before the melt-down. Imagine now. Wealthpoint argues that millennials: '…have been nickel-and-dimed through a wide variety of services, and they value simple, transparent, low-cost services.'[55]

Millennials have also driven the growth of Wealthfront, an alternative to traditional financial advisers who frequently steer clients towards their own firm's financial products. In contrast, Wealthfront has mimicked, in algorithmic form, the portfolio investment strategies of the most sophisticated wealth managers (e.g., rebalancing portfolios, tax-loss harvesting), traditionally available only to very-high-net-worth individuals.

Hanft goes on to offer a word of warning to the financial industry that could just as easily be applied to the health care industry. "The giants of financial service haven't seen the [volcanic] shifts that travel, media, entertainment and home thermostats have. They will. Depending on who you are, the Ben Franklin generation is composed of 80 million Benedict Arnolds."

Industry giants may want to ignore this trend, but millennials are the canary in the coal mine, because the fact is everyone wants these features.

As Danny Chrichton, a venture capitalist investor at CRV— and a millennial—has said, "consumers want to be able to manage their finances from their phones and tablets while limiting their visits to bank branches and bank tellers. Plus, everyone hates bank fees, particularly their complexity and lack of transparency. The difference is that millennials are willing to shop elsewhere, because we are simply not going to accept that these are the only products on the market."[56]

Another example is of millennials forcing change is the newspaper industry. Millennials ignored newspapers as a source of news but, also as the de facto place to buy/sell items (Craigslist anyone?). Undermining classified ads, which were roughly half of newspaper profits, made newspapers a demonstrably worse product. Those profits previously supported the reporting that has declined sharply over the last 10 years. Many papers have even had to eliminate editions on some days, further accelerating the trend.

Health Care Priorities: Cost and Convenience

The health system parallels to newspaper classified ads are profit centers such as cardiac catheterization labs—sometimes nicknamed "cash labs" as they are also centers of overuse. Cardiac catheterization led to the development of wonderful interventions—angioplasty, coronary artery bypass grafts, stents—that revolutionized cardiology in the 20th century. Without question, this saved lives. But the fact that these procedures are grossly overused is no longer in question either.

Overuse in health care is not simply a matter of wasted resources, money, and time. It exposes patients to terrible harm— often including death. Here's what happened to one 52-year-old woman who came into an ER with chest pain after starting a new exercise regime. Shannon Brownlee, Senior Vice President of the Lown Institute, described the situation at the Health Care Town Hall Meeting at the Frontier Cafe in Brunswick, Maine on November 6, 2014:

"The emergency doctor thought it was almost certainly a pulled muscle, but just to be sure he ordered a new and special CT scan of the heart. It showed a little something, as these scans so often do, and so just to be sure he sent her to the cath lab. There was nothing wrong with her heart until they perforated her aorta. They did an emergency bypass from which she recovered; but then she had graft bypass rejection and she had to have her heart replaced. This is a person who came into the emergency room with a pulled muscle."

Cath labs are no longer the sound investment they once were. Millennials, more than previous generations, want to know all the diagnostic and treatment possibilities when they're sick or injured and are more likely to select lower-cost, less invasive treatment options. This is also what most people of all generations want when given full information. Again, millennials are just the drivers.

Given their insistence on new ways of doing business on every front, it's not surprising that millennials are avoiding the ill-designed norms in health care. For example, selecting a doctor. It's not that millennials aren't loyal to their physicians when convenient, but they're far more willing than boomers to "doctor shop" until they are satisfied. They're looking for same-day appointments, online scheduling, easy access to their medical records, and the option to text or email the doctor between visits, according to KQED's Chrissy Farr.[57]

The vast majority of people who use ZocDoc—a website that helps individuals schedule doctor's visits—are millennials. Many of the doctors who have signed up on ZocDoc offer text and email communication, as well as weekend and evening appointments.

Retail clinics, typically found in national pharmacy chains like Walgreens and CVS, are another innovation being embraced by cost- and convenience-conscious millennials. Between 2006 and 2014, the number of retail clinics in the United States grew from 200 to 1800, while visits grew sevenfold to 1.5 million.[58] A PNC health care survey found that 34 percent of people ages 18 to 34 prefer retail clinics—about double the rate of 17 percent for baby boomers and 15 percent for older seniors.[59]

New Benefits Choices for Smart Employers

Millennials may be more interested than their parents in getting the most for their health care dollar, but nearly three in four of them are confused about their benefit options, according to a 2016 Harris Poll. And almost half would rather clean out their email than research those options.[60]

Why is this important to you and your company? Because that same survey shows that 76 percent of millennials say health care benefits strongly factor in their decision about where to work.[61]

Millennials are now the biggest portion of the workforce and will be 75 percent of it in 12 years.[62] The time has come for benefits brokers to fulfill their promise and guide their clients towards developing new benefits programs optimized for millennials.

For example, smart employers can shift their workforce to a higher-performing benefits package through tiers that introduce changes. Under this strategy, the old "get less, pay more," status quo package becomes "Tier 2." The new benefits offering is "Tier 1" and is the default package for new employees.

This is the millennials' moment. They're not alone, but will suffer the devastating consequences of an out-of-control health care system more than anyone. When millennials rise to the occasion, I believe they'll be remembered as the Greatest Generation of the 21st century.

CASE STUDY

ROSEN HOTELS & RESORTS

In my experience speaking with many companies who have beat the health care cost beast, there has been one recurring theme: Either the CEO or CFO took the lead—and did so knowing that success involves weaving employees into the reinvention process rather than trying to pull the wool over their eyes.

Harris Rosen is the founder, COO and president of Rosen Hotels & Resorts, a small regional chain in Orlando, Florida. Though he's not a health care expert, he intuitively knew what PwC data famously showed: half of health care spending doesn't add value.[63] In a business of ups and downs in which staff costs are a major factor, Rosen surrounded himself with a special executive team to tackle this challenge.

To date, they've adopted more Health Rosetta components than any other company I know, saving approximately $315 million on health care costs since 1971 and spend 50 percent lest per capita than the average employer. If all employers followed suit, we could conservatively remove $500 billion of waste from health care and shift it to more productive sectors of the economy.

Their plan has also grown from 500 to 5,700 lives. They have a highly culturally, racially, socioeconomically, and demographically diverse employee base, including many immigrants that often have not had regular access to care before. Yet single coverage for the average employee is only $18.75 per week for benefits that include medical, dental, and pharmacy and, as you'll see below, are better than most of us have ever had.

Rosen also uses focus groups and surveys to match up programs with employee needs, and they continuously refine their programs. Here are a few elements of what makes their program successful.

- They have a comprehensive, onsite 12,000-sf medical center that provides access to many routine health care services, far more than typical primary care. They even outfit it with used but modern and functional medical equipment for 10 to 15 cents on the dollar. Employees are able to visit the center "on the clock," thus removing a major barrier to receiving care.
- They take great care of individuals, hiring health coaches and nurses to serve as coaches and navigators throughout a medical journey. They use robust, evidence-based approaches to case management, in-patient care management, care transitions, and medication compliance management.
- They have eschewed the blunt instrument approaches most employers use to cut costs (high copays, deductibles) in favor of $5 office visit copays, zero copays for 90 percent of pharmaceuticals, and no co-insurance. Where necessary, they offer free transportation to appointments to further remove barriers.
- Company events serve food approved by nutritionists and the director of health services. They also offer cooking courses.
- They offer the most effective kind of wellness programs for free, including onsite stretching and exercise (e.g., Zumba, kick-boxing, walking programs, spinning, boot camp), flu shots and vaccinations, family planning, educational materials, nutritional services, and health fairs and physicals on a schedule informed by the US Preventive Services Task Force, which is far more conservative than workplace wellness vendors push.
- They provide free health screenings for colon cancer, diabetes, breast cancer (onsite mammograms), high cholesterol, hypertension, and sexually transmitted diseases, along with

visits from registered dietitians. Key to this is that it's based on evidence-based guidelines from organizations like the US Preventive Services Task Force to minimize misdiagnosis and overtreatment.

- They have a zero tolerance policy for tobacco use and do random drug and tobacco testing.
- They have a mandatory stretching program for housekeepers and other employees with a higher risk of injury, reducing injuries by 25 percent.
- Fifty-six percent of their employees' pregnancies are high risk as a result of high rates of advanced maternal age, diabetes, hypertension, and HIV. The company is very proactive about helping employees manage pregnancies (a premature birth can cost $500,000).
- The company cafeteria provides discounts for healthier foods to reduce consumption of unhealthier foods, e.g., discounts on salads. The dietitian and director of health services analyze employee cafeteria offerings for portion size and nutritional benefit. They also use signage to educate employees about nutrition, use smaller plates to control portion sizes, and limit fried food.
- They focus on better management of chronic conditions and have even seen a drop in development of new chronic conditions. This is especially important for workers coming from developing countries that often have complex diseases.

Rosen is partnering with other businesses in their community to expand this approach, demonstrating that it's worth ruffling a few feathers to gain the dual benefit of lower costs and a healthier, more satisfied workforce. The ripple effects extend well beyond the company, boosting employee well-being and their broader community's economy. For example, in an industry that sees employee turnover approaching 60 percent, Rosen has turnover in the low teens.

Rosen pays for full time employees' college tuition after five years of employment. They also pay state college tuition for employees' children after just three years of employment.

They've also used money that would have been overspent on health care to fuel a range of creative philanthropy. Rosen started by paying for preschool in the underserved, once crime-ridden Tangelo Park neighborhood in Orlando. He's also continued to fund various programs to help those kids develop, such as paying for their college education in full (tuition, room/board, and books). The results have been breathtaking.

- Crime has been reduced by 63 percent
- High school graduation rates went from 45 percent to nearly 100 percent
- College graduation rates are 77 percent above the national average

The cost over 24 years of the Tangelo Park program has been $11 million—roughly the amount Rosen saves in one year. Recently Rosen has agreed to adopt another underserved community called Parramore, which is five times the size of Tangelo Park.

For Harris Rosen, the approach is simple: Get involved, care for your people.

Part II

How and Why Employers Are Getting Fleeced

The health care industry has been extremely deft at persuading employers to accept hyperinflating costs you wouldn't accept in any other area of your operations. In this part of the book, we highlight the most common ways the industry ensures their revenue and profits grow inexorably. We delve into three of the biggest areas that are least understood.

For example, it would be logical to assume that an insurance company could aggregate their buying power to get your organization a better deal. While this certainly is possible and can happen to an extent, just the opposite generally happens. The much-vaunted PPO networks actually ensure that you pay for the privilege of greatly overpaying for health care services. Then there's criminal fraud. While it's impossible not to know about cybercrime and cybersecurity issues, most CEOs don't know that as much as 10 percent of all claims their company pays are fraudulent as a result of a lack of oversight. Finally, we debunk the notion that workplace wellness programs will have any demonstrable impact on costs. While there may be reasons to have workplace wellness programs, cost reduction isn't one of them.

CHAPTER 5

7 TRICKS USED TO REDISTRIBUTE PROFITS FROM YOUR ORGANIZATION TO THE HEALTH CARE INDUSTRY

The health care industry has been remarkably effective at extracting as much money as possible from the U.S. economy. Employers and individuals pick up the majority of this tab.[64] Unlike virtually every other input in your supply chain where the value proposition improves every year, the norm in health care for decades is to pay more and get less. Unlike nearly every other industry, health care hasn't had a productivity gain in 20 years.[65]

In other words, for the last two decades there has been a redistribution "tax" from highly efficient companies to the least productive industry in America.[66] On top of this, the waste is beginning to potentially create personal legal exposure for you and your financial and HR executives that is snapping many of your colleagues into action. Here's what you need to learn first about what they know.

Costly Health Care Industry Tricks

This list is not exhaustive but does highlight some of the largest cost issues. Once you know what to look for, you can overcome these issues by applying the strategies and lessons from Parts III and IV of this book.

While these tricks exist in both fully-insured and self-insured companies, the ability to take corrective action is largely limited to self-insured companies. Understanding that fully-insured employers already bear much of the risk of being self-insured, but without the benefits, helps simplify the decision to go self-insured. If you're a fully-insured employer and have higher-than-expected claims in one year, your insurance carrier will work to get as much back as possible in subsequent years through larger premium increases.

Employers with well-managed plans are already reducing health benefits spending by 20 percent or more with better results—directing savings toward higher uses, like cash reserves, profits, R&D, better wages, new benefits, or profit sharing.

And let me say before we plunge into the dark side of health care that there are many, many exceptional health care organizations and professionals—insurance carriers, plan administrators, benefits brokers, physicians, hospitals, nursing homes—that don't employ these unethical practices. Plus, a vanguard of doctors and others are leading the way to stamp out the bad actors for good. We already met a few of these rebels in Chapter 1.

Trick #1: Directing Patients to the Most Expensive Treatment Options, Even if They're Not the Most Effective

People often raise the specter of rationing care. In reality, it's overuse (i.e., unnecessary and potentially harmful care) that leads to reduced access by squandering enormous financial resources that would be better used for individuals who actually need care and can't get it.

I asked Garrison Bliss, MD, the founder of the first direct primary care practice—a model for employers and individuals to directly contract with primary care clinicians in high-value, cost-reducing arrangements—how they were able to achieve a 30 to 50 percent reduction in surgeries. The answer was remarkably simple: Let people choose.

For example, one of the most common reasons people go to the doctor is back pain, one of the most overtreated symptoms around. Having personally experienced searing back pain, I would do almost anything to make it go away. If I'm told that surgery and opioids are the only way to go, that's what I'll probably do. However, it turns out that physical therapy is very often more effective than surgery. According to Bliss, individuals will virtually always choose the least invasive and safest treatments when they're clearly told about the pros and cons of effective potential options.

This doesn't typically happen though. A primary reason is that hospital-employed primary care doctors receive financial incentives to refer patients to high-margin specialty practices. In Chapter 9, we'll learn that 90 percent of back surgeries performed at Virginia Mason Hospital & Medical Center were unnecessary and that musculoskeletal (MSK) procedures account for roughly 20 percent of all health care spending. By simply deploying an evidence-based MSK program, a large tire manufacturer improved its earnings by 1.7 percent. Had it been able to get all of its employees who have MSK issues into the program, its positive earnings impact could have been 5 percent. How many corporate initiatives can increase earnings by 5 percent?

Trick #2: Turning Primary Care into a Milk-in-the-Back-of-the-Store Loss Leader

Dr. Paul Grundy, IBM's chief medical officer and director of health care transformation, shared with me how IBM undertook a two-year study from 2005-2006 of its $2 billion annual global health care spend. The results reinforced what many already knew—a strong bias against primary care that has been highly effective at undermining this valuable resource in favor of higher-cost specialty care. One consequence of this is the 10-minute primary care appointment, which leaves little time to delve into the root cause of whatever issues bring an individual to the office. This pressures physicians to take shortcuts to satisfying patients—ordering a test or prescribing a drug.

This pattern is also a key driver of the opioid crisis, along with well-intended patient satisfaction surveys that feature questions about the patient's happiness with the pain control measures they were given. A provider's scores on these surveys is an increasingly significant factor in how much they're reimbursed for government-sponsored programs like Medicare.

Trick #3: Using Intentionally Bewildering and Absurd Drug Pricing

Drug pricing is bewildering by design and an increasingly large share of your benefits spending. It's part of the strategy to get away with exorbitant prices. Pharmacy benefit management (PBM) firms are well-known for hidden fees, shell game pricing, and taking drug manufacturers' money to promote specific medications.[67] With the breathtaking spike in specialty drug prices in recent years, these practices are costing shareholders, employees, and employers dearly.

Recently, two very well-known PBMs added a brand drug called Duexis to their formularies, which currently sells for more than $4,000 for a 90-day supply. Duexis is a combination of two drugs you likely have in your medicine cabinet that together cost only a few bucks—ibuprofen and famotidine (common household names, Motrin and Pepcid). Vimovo is another expensive combination drug that is just delayed-release omeprazole (Prilosec) and naproxen sodium (Aleve).

PBM consultant CrystalClearRx pulled data to show the drastic difference in pricing for a 90-day supply of comparable drugs and identical dosages for these two brand drugs and their generic counterparts.[68]

Duexis	Ibuprofen+Famotidine
$4,680	$20 to $40
Vimovo	Omeprazole + Naproxen Sodium
$2,279	$20 to $40

In these cases, the brand drugs are 50 to 234 times more expensive for functionally the same drug. PBMs are incentivized to add these kinds of drugs to formularies so they can tout big discounts off high-cost drug costs. It also lets them capture high-margin revenue from hidden rebates they receive from drug manufacturers. Rebates are a form of arbitrage where PBMs receive money back from drug companies on each claim for a particular drug. They typically either don't refund this to you at all or only partially refund it.

PBMs are also sometimes owned insurance carriers and are not held to the margin requirements the ACA imposes on the insurance carrier. The PBM reaps enormous profits, while allowing the carrier to cry "poor" and raise your rates.

Enough said.

Trick #4: Not Suggesting Management Strategies for Rare but Astronomical Claims

Benefits manager Tom Emerick, co-author of *Cracking Health Costs: How to Cut Your Company's Health Costs and Provide Employees Better Care*, pointed out how outlier claims are the biggest driver of the health care cost explosion. During his time with BP and Walmart, Emerick typically found that 6 percent of employees in a given year accounted for 80 percent of company medical costs. Walmart set up a Centers of Excellence program to address the most expensive cases, in which they send employees and family members needing heart, spine, and transplant surgeries to six of the most highly rated and thus most cost-effective health care organizations for free care—if they need it.

Often they don't. Emerick's book explains how Walmart found that 40 percent of planned organ transplants at local hospitals were deemed medically unnecessary when their employees visited top-notch providers such as Mayo Clinic for a second opinion. In a study published in 2017, Mayo Clinic reported that as many as 88 percent of patients who visit the clinic for a second opinion on a complex procedure go home with a new or refined diagnosis—changing their care plan and potentially saving their lives.

Dialysis management is another source of extraordinary bills. More than 25,000,000 Americans have chronic kidney disease, and 100,000 start dialysis each year. This is inevitable, but employers can turn the huge disparity among costs for the same services, from $100,000 to more than $500,000, to their advantage by scouting out the lowest-cost, high-quality services.

Trick #5: Hiding the Use of Accessory—and Often Out-of-Network—Physicians

It happens all the time: You have the insurance carrier's authorization for your physician, who is part of your plan's PPO network, to perform a procedure like a surgery or colonoscopy. Everything seems straightforward—until you get the bill and see charges from an anesthetist, a pathologist, or a radiologist you don't know and who turns out to be out-of-network, is not subject to negotiated discounts, and requires paying a larger out-of-pocket share because they're out-of-network.

This is what happened to Gap Inc. and it had much larger consequences than just paying more for care. Their HR leaders have been named in a lawsuit for breach of fiduciary duty for not applying proper care in managing their health plan.[69] (See Chapter 19 for more discussion of employer fiduciary responsibilities issues under ERISA.) Some employers have tried to head off this situation with much-touted "wrap networks," designed primarily to cover employees who need care when they're away from home. But the wrap network rates are typically significantly higher than the rates under your PPO network. And it may actually cost more to file a claim under a wrap network than to have your benefits administrator negotiate a disputed claim.

Trick #6: Delivering Inappropriate Oncology Treatment

Sadly, way too much cancer treatment is unproven. Cancer centers may not follow evidence-based treatment guidelines for certain cancers and too often have limited regard for the devastating side effects patients experience during and after treatment. Also, financial conflicts are rampant at cancer centers, which may not inform individuals and their families about costs, copayments, and co-insurance before treatment.

Dr. Otis Brawley, MD, chief medical officer for the American Cancer Society and author of *How We Do Harm: A Doctor Breaks Ranks about Being Sick in America,* famously said that "the talk should not be about rationing care but about rational health care." He described taking over the care of a patient with colon cancer that was dumped by their doctor after losing their insurance. Dr. Brawley found that the patient was on a chemotherapy regimen that was 15 years out of date and taking unnecessary drugs on which the first "greedy" doctor was receiving a substantial markup.

"I've seen so many times," wrote Brawley, "where doctors really have failed to evolve and… learn as the profession and the scientific evidence have changed over time."[70]

Putting his experience in context, the *BMJ Quality and Safety Journal* has estimated that 28 percent of cancers are misdiagnosed in the first place.[71]

Trick #7: Suppressing Quality and Safety Data

Not only is it statistically safer to be in an airplane than a hospital, it's also statistically far safer to deliberately jump *out* of that plane (skydiving) than to be in a hospital.[72] Surprised? That's just how the health care industry wants it.

Industry lobbying power—health care lobbyists outspend the oil, financial, and defense industries *combined*—is on full display when it comes to hiding quality and safety information from the public.[73] Fortunately, other people are determined to dig that information out and get it to you.

Leapfrog, an independent nonprofit founded by leading employers and health care experts, promotes health care transparency through data collection and public reporting initiatives. You can check Leapfrog Hospital Safety Grades online for your local hospitals.[74] Their quality grades are based on a voluntary annual hospital survey they conduct, but only around 1,800 hospitals of 5,564 in the U.S. currently participate. They also publish safety grades based on publicly available data and the survey results for participating hospitals.

You can also go to Medicare's Hospital Compare, which provides data on the 4,000+ hospitals that are Medicare-certified, to find out how hospitals in your area are performing on some 60 measures, everything from serious complication rates to the percent of patients who report being given information about what to do after discharge and during recovery.[75]

You can also find safety and other data about physicians at Vitals.com, RateMDs.com, and HealthGrades.com.

None of these ratings efforts are entirely satisfactory, some less so than others, but it's a start. More important, you can ask questions. As an employer, it's your job to find out as much as you can about the care available to your employees and you have the ability to do so—no matter what the industry says.

CHAPTER 6

PPO NETWORKS DELIVER VALUE—AND OTHER FLAWED ASSUMPTIONS THAT CRUSH YOUR BOTTOM LINE

A lbert Einstein famously said, "We can't solve problems by using the same kind of thinking we used when we created them." And yet, this is exactly what health care does over and over.

Baked into our thinking about health benefits administration are many assumptions that turn out to be flawed on deeper examination—at best outdated, at worst outrageous.

Here are three that are doing your organization and employees serious harm.

1. Your broker works for you*
2. Insurance carriers want to drive down costs and PPO networks deliver the best pricing available
3. Auto-adjudication of claims is always good

---

*   There are certainly some excellent brokers that do their best for employers, but the overwhelming majority have undisclosed conflicts of interest that favor of insurance carriers. In this book, the term benefits consultant or advisor refers to people who provide a broader range of services and expertise than simply signing up clients on behalf of a carrier. Many of them bring a more sophisticated brand of professionalism to their clients. See Chapter 11 for a more complete treatment of this critical subject.

Together, these three flawed assumptions may seem minor, but together add up to significant costs and damage to your bottom line, your employees' bottom line, and your employees' health. Luckily, knowing about them is half the battle to counteracting them.

Flawed Assumption #1: Your Broker Works for You.

Organizations often treat brokers as a buyer's agent, but the reality is that their financial incentives typically make them a seller's agent for your insurance carrier and other health benefits vendors. Benefits consulting is a $22 billion industry, and insurance companies are the source for the majority of that revenue.[76]

According to industry veterans, over 90 percent of the compensation models for brokers conflict with your objectives, because their income increases as overall per capita health care spending increases. In a proper model, one would expect exactly the opposite. Compensation should *decrease* as low-value spending increases. Over the last few decades of consistent health care spending increases, status quo brokers have won big while employers and their employees have lost.

We've found that most disturbing to CFOs and CEOs is that brokers generally don't disclose a significant portion of their compensation. For example, insurance carriers and other vendors work to retain clients by tying broker commission and bonus programs to the *total* business the broker places with the carrier, not just your business. Brokers must typically clear a specific threshold of business each year to get these bonuses. *Your business is just one piece of the total, but keeping it with the same carrier can boost the broker's total compensation by 50 percent or more.* Because this compensation isn't specific to you, status quo brokers will often claim they've disclosed fees and commissions. But they are actually only disclosing your *account-specific* fees and commissions that may not even be the most significant piece of their overall compensation.

Another way insurance carriers enforce loyalty is 30-day cancellation clauses in broker contracts that let carriers drop brokers on 30-day notice. If a broker gets over half of their entire compensation from a specific carrier—a common situation that can include annuity-type compensation built up over years—you can imagine how potent the threat to cancel the broker's agreement is.

Flawed Assumption #2: Insurance Carriers Want to Drive Down Costs and PPO Networks Deliver the Best Pricing.

Much of pricing in health care is set as a percentage of Medicare pricing. Why? Because Medicare uses a rigorous process to develop pricing that takes into account actual hospital costs (which are often inflated, but we cover that elsewhere) and market variances. The average PPO network pricing is 2.6 times Medicare rates or, as it is often called, "260 percent of Medicare." While there are some markets where average commercial payer pricing is lower, there are many more where the number is significantly greater—as high as 1,000 percent of Medicare in some places.[77]

To get a deeper perspective, I spoke with Mike Dendy, Vice Chairman and CEO of Advanced Medical Pricing Solutions, Inc. (AMPS), a health care cost management company. A 26-year veteran of the health care industry, Dendy was previously Chairman/CEO of HPS Paradigm Administrators, an independent third party administrator (TPA) services company that manages both private and public sector plans. Before that, he was the head of the community health system business at Memorial Hospital in Savannah, Georgia.

Dendy's company manages a large volume of claims. On average, he says they find that hospitals bill services (called gross billed charges) at about 550 percent of Medicare and that the major insurance carrier PPO network discounts are approximately 50 percent off those prices.

"It is amazing how little employers know about what they pay. I recently met with a Fortune 100 company that has 110,000 U.S.-based employees and asked their human resources vice president how much they were paying for health care relative to the Medicare benchmark. He had no clue and was flabbergasted when I gave him the answer. The BUCAs [Blue Cross, United-healthcare, Cigna, and Aetna] hide that information, of course."

In comparison, employers who properly manage their health care spend will often pay roughly 150 percent of Medicare rates. Their logic is that the government has arrived at a price that would enable health care organizations to sustain themselves, so hospitals should be willing to take a 50 percent premium on top of that. Some will accept 120 percent or less.

However, most employers play the PPO's "discount" game without question. There is a "wink, wink, nod, nod" exercise that insurance carriers and health providers go through to arrive at a baseline PPO network price, which allows insurance carriers to say they "negotiated" a larger discount, say 52 percent. This makes it appear that the network can get you a better deal than you can on your own. I'll give you a 99 percent discount on anything if I get to choose the undiscounted price.

To add insult to injury, PPO networks charge access fees of $12-$20 per employee per month (PEPM) for what you might call the privilege of overpaying for health care services. The story insurance carriers continue to push on employers is that their employees won't be able to see a doctor or be admitted into a hospital outside the PPO network relationship. This is every bit as ludicrous as it sounds. Care provider organizations are often eager to develop direct payment arrangements that are far better than typical PPO rates.

Flawed Assumption #3: Auto-Adjudication of Claims Is Always Good

Auto-adjudication is the term used to describe automatic payment of claims. Claims administrators will highlight one of three specific benefits, how your employees won't be hassled with bills, it's a sign of efficiency, or it's based on sophisticated algorithms—typically all three. However, the best way to describe auto-adjudication is that you're giving another organization a blank check to withdraw money from your treasury based on minimal information that may or may not even be accurate.

Claims administrators from the largest national insurance companies to the smallest mom and pop shops essentially all follow the same process. They receive a useless Uniform Bill (UB) from a hospital as an invoice, deduct the PPO discount from the total price, then pay the claim.

Figure 9 is an anonymized UB provided to me by Dendy. This one-page UB represents the entire invoice submitted by the hospital on this $323,000 claim. Note that 322 units of laboratory—completely unspecified—are billed at $157,808. No one in their right mind would ever accept such minimal detail if they're spending their own money. And yet the claims administrator in this case was prepared to write the check if AMPS had not intervened.

Further, BUCA administrators often charge $30 to $60 PEPM to pay bills using this see-nothing, know-nothing method. Pretty good gig if you can get it. Large insurance carriers typically auto-adjudicate 90 percent or more of all claims.[78] Dendy's firm recently intervened on behalf of a Fortune 100 company on a hospital bill for well over $2 million. Even he was shocked to learn that the claims administrator was ready to pay on the basis of the single-page UB.

It's no surprise that claims administrators often have clauses in their agreements with employers that would only fly in health care. What's surprising is that so many employers are willing to sign them. For example, contracts stipulate that claims data is proprietary and owned by the carrier, meaning you don't get to see your own claims data. Sometimes they'll use HIPAA privacy as a smokescreen prevent you from having your data analyzed by an outside party, an issue HIPAA effectively accommodates.

Second, claims administrators will insist on extremely limited claim audit clauses. One large company I'm aware of with more than two million claims per year had an audit clause that gave it the right to audit just 200 claims of the administrator's choosing and only on the carrier's premises. That's 0.01 percent of all claims for what is often a company's first or second largest expense after payroll.

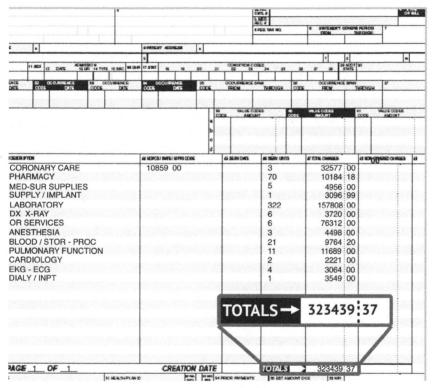

Figure 9. Actual deidentified uniform bill provided by Dendy.

Limited audit clauses often reflect an agreement between insurance carriers and health care providers. The insurance carrier will sign a PPO agreement with a hospital that, absurdly, doesn't allow the carrier itself to audit claims. The alleged reason is that it's all part of the give and take in negotiations, in which the carrier "demands" a certain discount in exchange for not auditing the claims they pay from that hospital.[79]

This dynamic is why transparent medical markets featuring direct relationships between employers and hospitals have arisen (See Chapter 15 to learn more). By directly contracting with a health care provider, employers can secure significant savings. More direct, streamlined payment makes it valuable for high-value health care providers as well.

CASE STUDY

CITY OF MILWAUKEE

John Torinus

B ecause the economic pain of out-of-control medical costs is so high and Federal Government reforms are so slow, school districts, counties, and municipalities are moving on their own to find savings across the four major platforms for containing health care spending: self-insurance, consumer-driven incentives and disincentives, onsite proactive primary care, and value-based purchasing.

The City of Milwaukee, Wisconsin, with 6,500 employees is one spectacular example. The city has held its health care costs *flat* for the last five years, stopping its previous hyper-inflationary trend of eight to 9 percent annual increases. Milwaukee spent $139 million on health care in 2011 before switching over to a self-insured plan in 2012. Costs dropped to $102 million in 2012 and have stayed at about that level ever since—even in the face of 6 percent annual inflation for nationally employer plans over the same period.

If the old trend had continued, health costs for 2016 would have been about $200 million, double what they actually were. Instead, the cost savings have had many additional positive ramifications: raises for county employees, no layoffs, flat employee premium contributions, better health outcomes for employees and their families, improved productivity, lower absenteeism, and less pressure to raise taxes.

Michael Brady, benefits manager, led this intelligent management approach in close collaboration with the mayor, city council, and unions. As with other enlightened group plans, there are many moving parts. Here's a sampling.

- Twelve percent of costs are paid by employees, but these have stayed flat because employees are making better decisions about family health and care purchases.
- An onsite wellness center and workplace clinic, headed by nurse practitioners, have sharply reduced hospital admissions. Onsite physical therapy was added last year. These services are free for employees and spouses.
- Relatively low deductibles (now $750 per single employee and $1,500 per family) were installed to create a consumer-friendly environment.
- Coinsurance was set at 10 percent for members who use UnitedHealthcare's Premium Provider program, which uses only doctors designated as top doctors by UnitedHealthcare. Coinsurance is 30 percent for providers outside that group. This tiered approach, aimed at improving health outcomes, is a form of value-based purchasing.
- Participants in the city's wellness program can earn $250 in a health account. Good progress has been made on hypertension and smoking (now 12 percent vs. U.S. average of 14 percent), but, as with other employers, there's not been as much traction on obesity. There have been some improvements on chronic disease management of diabetes.*
- A $200 ER copay has cut nonurgent ER visits by 300 per year.

---

*   *While workplace wellness programs typically have no or negative ROI (see Chapter 8), approaches that use solid clinical evidence to address costly chronic illness and procedures without encouraging overtreatment are sometimes lumped into the same category as typical workplace wellness programs. However, they are highly different in goals, execution, and results.*

- An intense program to reduce injuries, started in 2008, has resulted in a 70 percent drop in injury hours off work. The program has saved $10 million per year compared to the previous trend line.
- Milwaukee now spends about $15,000 per employee per year, well below the national average and not too far off the $13,000 at the best private companies.

Government entities are not known for bold innovation, so this track record is an eye-opener, especially in a unionized environment. The results, said Brady, are nothing short of amazing "considering changes in the city's workforce demographics and the challenging environmental hazards that city employees regularly face."

These changes have taken place at the same time that the nation as a whole has experienced much more disappointing progress from federal reforms, e.g., much higher deductibles for plans sold on ACA exchanges, double-digit premium rises for employers in many states, and a cost to the Federal Government of about $5,000 per subsidized plan member per year.

Clearly, most of the meaningful reform of the economic chaos from health care in this country is coming from self-insured employers, like the City of Milwaukee.

John Torinus is chairman of Serigraph Inc., a Wisconsin-based graphics parts manufacturer, and author of "The Company That Solved Health Care."

CHAPTER 7

CRIMINAL FRAUD IS MUCH BIGGER THAN YOU THINK

Most of us think of fraud in health care as the domain of a few bad doctors, similar to what exists in virtually any human enterprise. In reality, it adds up to a staggering $300 billion annually, roughly 10 percent of all spending.[80] It is also remarkably straightforward to stop, but only if claims administrators—those actually able to stop it—do so. Yet most lack the financial incentives to do so, only making basic attempts after-the-fact that are like trying to stop fraud with a musket in an era of unmanned drones.

More alarming is that significant fraudulent gains may go to foreign actors. The world's cybercrime hotspots are all outside the United States, according to *Time*.[81] *Infoworld*[82] explained why hackers want your health care data. Among other reasons, it has a much longer shelf-life than other targets like credit cards, which become useless once a consumer gets a new card. However, medical and insurance information has value for years.

If fraud weren't bad enough, the fact that it is leaving the U.S. economy makes it even more of an economic drain. Stopping fraud would be like providing the American economy with an annual recurring $300 Billion economic stimulus. Over two-plus years, that stimulus would be equivalent to the massive stimulus at the beginning of the 2008 financial crisis.

Health Insurance Carriers Are Acting Rationally

There are two key drivers of insurance carrier economics that are relevant to understanding criminal fraud (These issues were covered more thoroughly in Chapter 3).

1. Anything that drives health care spending upward, even paying fraudulent claims, economically benefits insurance carriers and claims administrators.
2. The ACA's Medical Loss Ratio cap requires that 80 to 85 percent of premium dollars go to care, not marketing and overhead. Because fraud prevention isn't considered care, this reduces economic incentives to invest in it. Technology and other solutions that prevent fraud are just another expense that eats into this government-mandated margin cap.

Even if an employer is self-insured, there is a spillover effect as insurance carriers are generally motivated to invest in technologies and services that fuel revenue increases rather than reduce spending. In other words, there isn't a strong enough motivation to root out waste and fraud.

It's important to highlight how only-in-health-care dynamics open the door to large-scale fraud in the first place. Pay and chase programs (covered in Chapter 3) are like paying a napping guard extra money to chase a criminal who just cleaned out the bank vault. According to private conversations with industry insiders, claims administrators are doing little to stop fraudulent claims. Instead, after allowing fraudulent claims to be paid, they chase after the thieves, receiving 30 to 40 percent of what they recover.

The Data Problem

More fraud creates more upward premium pressure that economically benefits insurance carriers, but takes from everyone else. The root of this is the U.S. health care system's current claims methodology that is fraught with disconnection and a lack of transparency and control between employers, patients, providers, and insurers. In contrast, the financial industry has been using preventive methodologies for decades, giving the consumers both security assurances and control over their credit, resulting in much lower credit card fraud rates—just 0.07 percent of total volume.[83] This means the cost of health care fraud is 14,285 percent higher than credit card fraud.

The comparably large and equally complex health care industry has generally avoided adopting similar prevention methodologies, erroneously citing a billing and payment system that is too complex for it to work. As a result, employers have resorted to taking a reactive and largely ineffective approach to recovering money after claims have been paid. This "pay and chase" method delivers a dismal average return rate of only 2 to 4 percent—enough to say something is being done, but a drop in the bucket compared to the full magnitude of the problem.[84]

When it comes to auditing claims to identify fraud, insurance carriers have historically relied on sampling methodologies to determine whether or not the claims process is sufficiently secure. Health care claims reviews are done independently on a per-visit basis and are largely a paper-driven process. This allows fraud and waste to fall through the cracks because there is so much disparate data and no standard format for how it is analyzed and processed.

Separately, the industry has pushed to auto-adjudicating claims as quickly as possible, a good thing if not for the lack of correspondingly robust implementation of fraud (and waste and abuse) detection and prevention technologies and processes. "The current claims process is predicated on rapid processing of health care transactions with little real emphasis on the legitimacy and accuracy of the claims themselves," states Scott Haas, Senior Vice President of Wells Fargo Insurance Services USA, Inc. "The Department of Labor claim processing regulations emphasize the time frame in which claim payers must either pay or deny claims. The regulations assume payers are actually diligent in assessing whether or not the claims require any form of audit or scrutiny."

Such antiquated processes, disparate data, and unintended regulatory consequences creates a macro-situation ripe with subjective interpretation of claims and claims data, often making the eventual reconciliation of plan coverage and payment too late. Often, this also leads to legitimate claims being denied erroneously, further adding to the frustration of everyone involved in the claims paying process. It's a costly failure for everyone.

Connecting the Data Points

Fraud only becomes visible when you connect all of the care participants and events. Here are two real-life examples I've seen.

- A woman undergoing multiple hysterectomies
- A man getting multiple circumcisions from different providers in a single week

Technically, these cases each meet all of the basic claims review and adjudication criteria (e.g., all of the fields are filled out and don't have dates where numbers should be or numbers where text should be). Therefore, they pass the sufficiency test and the claims are paid. However, it's obvious that both are fraud.

The problems from not connecting the dots can be less obvious than multiple instances of one-in-a-lifetime procedures. One example is a case where four doctors provided the same service to the same patient during the same procedure. When each provider's claim is viewed independently, the claim meets sufficiency criteria and thus passes the paid claims review test. But the total amount they're charging far exceeds the total allowable amount for the contract.

Big data and technologies similar to those used for services like Visa Fraud Protection make it possible to identify, predict, and minimize fraud through advanced analytics for detecting fraud and validating claim accuracy and consistency.

Payment integrity technology is available that can analyze disparate claims data at the employer, patient, provider, and insurance carrier levels, simultaneously across all health care systems. Such technology-based systems can connect a patient's behavior with the relevant physician behavior. For example, a patient who has had a hysterectomy in the past and suddenly has pregnancy-related claims should be flagged. By contrast, the financial services industry has used similar behavior patterns both at the retailer and consumer levels to identify purchases that do not fit the consumer's normal behavior since the earliest days of credit cards.

Payment integrity solutions break the reactive "pay and chase" approach with innovative solutions that could nearly eliminate fraud, making it unnecessary for employers to chase after already spent money. These types of solutions will play a critical role in reducing the exorbitant amounts of money lost to fraud and waste in the health care system every year.

CHAPTER 8

ARE WORKPLACE WELLNESS PROGRAMS HAZARDOUS TO YOUR HEALTH?

One area of widespread spending that typically has little benefit—and no cost savings—is workplace wellness programs. To start, they're usually sold on mathematically impossible ROIs and undisclosed commission models that enormously benefit brokers. This has caused Al Lewis, former workplace wellness industry proponent turned leading critic, to offer a $2 million reward to anyone who can prove that the industry has reduced employers' medical claims costs enough to cover its $8 billion annual cost.[85] So far, his money is safe.

By way of background, Lewis was a workplace wellness industry insider, called one of the founding fathers of disease management.[86] Now, he's CEO of Quizzify, a provider of employee health literacy programs, and author of several best-selling books on measuring the outcomes of employee health improvement programs, especially workplace wellness programs (check out *Surviving Workplace Wellness* and *Why Nobody Believes the Numbers*).

Promoters place workplace wellness programs among the most important advances in medical history, equivalent in impact to vaccines and antibiotics (their words).[87] Detractors call it a "scam." An entire website, www.theysaidwhat.net, is devoted to exposing its many alleged lies and misdeeds.

Obviously, it can't be both a significant advance and total scam. It's critical to know which though, because there is a very specific distinction between workplace wellness programs and everything else in this book. Whereas everything else is an unfortunate byproduct of insuring your employees in today's status quo market, these programs are a totally optional undertaking.

Workplace wellness program fees typically cost employers $100 to $150 per employee per year. Plus a similar amount in employee incentives to encourage usage. Plus lost work time to participate in screening programs and complete health risk assessments. Plus administrative time to ensure compliance with relevant laws and regulations. Add these up and you start to see that the total costs are much more than just vendor fees. All this to generate great employee dissatisfaction, judging by the fact that a 2016 *Slate* article entitled "Workplace Wellness is a Sham" generated more shares than any other *Slate* article on either health care or the workplace that year.[88]

Lewis advocates a much simpler approach to preventive care, regular screenings based on well-established clinical guidelines developed by the U.S. Preventive Services Task Force (USPSTF), an independent, volunteer panel of national experts in prevention and evidence-based medicine.[89] To balance the harms of overscreening, misdiagnosis, and overtreatment against the benefits of early detection, the USPSTF guidelines recommend far fewer blood screenings, far less frequently than most vendors advocate. These guidelines are easily accessible through the Choosing Wisely initiative, a partnership between the American Board of Internal Medicine Foundation and *Consumer Reports* that seeks to advance a national dialogue on avoiding wasteful or unnecessary medical tests, treatments, and procedures.[90]

Promoters Undercut Their Own Data

Tellingly, promoters' own data consistently and convincingly undermine their claims, which is easily shown using facts, data, and basic arithmetic. Here are some examples to support this thesis—keep in mind that we're using what the industry says about itself.

1. A national leading workplace wellness program promoter's own conclusions and assertions have shown that a perfect workplace wellness program targeting cardiac care would have a negative ROI of $100 per employee per year.
2. An analysis in *Health Affairs* of Connecticut's workplace wellness program concluded that it increased costs. The state justified it by saying it increased the number of checkups, even though the US Preventive Services Task Force Guidelines and the *Journal of the American Medical Association* have concluded that checkups don't improve health and are more likely to find problems that don't exist.
3. The Health Enhancement Research Organization's—the wellness industry's trade association—own guidebook shows that workplace wellness programs don't generate positive ROI.
4. The industry's trade publication has published articles that conclude 90 to 95 percent of workplace wellness programs have no impact, that only poorly-designed clinical studies on programs show strong ROI, and that an editor concluded "Who cares about an ROI anyway?"
5. The data submitted by winners of the industry's top Koop award—which is selected by wellness industry executives—over the last couple of years show that they didn't save money and, in some cases, showed that health actually deteriorated.

These are just a few examples of many I could have selected. If you want to dive deeper, Appendix A has more detailed summaries for each.

The Bottom Line

I can only conclude two things from these examples.

First, there are no savings in conventional workplace wellness programs. Giving employees lots of time off to exercise might be a good idea for other reasons—just don't try to calculate savings from it.

Second, there's no getting around it. Many, if not most, vendors lie about ROI.

Money spent on workplace wellness programs—upwards of $100 to $150 per employee per year just for the vendor fees—is wasted. Plus, this doesn't include all the peripheral tangible and intangible costs, like time spent engaging in the programs. Further, the fees cover only the administrative medical expenses, not the expenses submitted via claims forms. Superfluous annual checkups urged by vendors probably double that figure. Employee incentives to get them to use programs likely double it again.

Speaking of ROI, the fastest way in this book to create a ROI is to reduce screening frequencies to follow established, age-appropriate, USPSTF guidelines. Not only will you avoid the expense, but you'll also avoid potentially harming your employees. Based on the data in this book alone, that would be a significant improvement over what is happening now.

Another possibility would be to explore the proposed 401W Savings Plan, which aligns incentives between employers and employees to work towards long-term health maintenance, while saving employers money and quite literally giving people financial responsibility for taking care of themselves.[91] It also increases employee retention, as well as program satisfaction.

Sound good so far? If you need one more reason to look into the 401W Savings Plan, here it is. As most people in the industry know, Al Lewis is the Mikey of wellness. He hates everything. But he likes this a lot.[92]

Yes, Virginia, There Are Workplace Wellness Programs That Work

Like ABC's Wide World of Sports, we've spanned the globe looking for workplace wellness programs that work. We 've found three.

First is Cummins, a diesel engine manufacturer with 55,000 employees. When *Fortune*, went looking for the best, this was the one they found.[93] After years of trying to "preach the gospel" of wellness with conventional screenings, Cummins realized it wasn't working. So they rebooted a new model with a "continuum" of services that employees could select from to reach their goals. Plus, much of what Cummins does is environmental—such as workplace design—so there is no need for employees to "opt in." Well-being comes to them.

For those who want to adopt a healthier lifestyle, Cummins offers many opt-in opportunities. This is in sharp contrast to conventional programs that try to make employees healthy whether they want it or not. No wonder they consistently make the *Fortune* list of the 100 best places to work.

Next, *Workforce* magazine highlighted the Hilliard County (OH) Schools.[94] Their wellness leader, Debbie Youngblood, had the insight that, for example, you can't teach employees to eat less sugar if they don't know where that sugar is hidden in the ingredients labels.

"It always surprises me," says Ms. Youngblood, "that we expect people to know how to achieve overall well-being. [Yet] we've given them very little opportunity to know, understand, and practice the things that might be beneficial."

For a third example, we turned to the very same Al Lewis who basically finds fault in everything workplace wellness and challenged him to come up with one. Surely, in all his travels, he had found a single program—just one—that worked. He thought for a minute and then said: "Wait a sec! The one I'm in, Boston College's, is great. They actually screen me according to guidelines. I mean, that shouldn't win them a Nobel Prize, but in this industry, it does.

"Plus, when I go in for my screen—every three years, just like the guidelines say—I'm always trying to find fault, but instead I am amazed at how good the guidance is. Totally up to date on carbs and fat, no telling me to get a PSA test or other inappropriate interventions, and knowledgeable staff. And no wonder. They get their program from Harvard Pilgrim Health Care, the top-ranked health plan in the country basically every year, according to the National Committee for Quality Assurance."

Part III

Doing It Right

*A*s we say on the Health Rosetta website, "Health care is already *fixed. Join us to replicate the fixes." Fortunately, whether private or public sector, rural or urban, small or large, employers in virtually every corner of the country have proven that they can reduce spending by 20 percent or more compare to average employers while significantly improving benefits programs. In this part of the book, we lay out the most important building blocks and mindsets. We explore how a transparent benefits advisor or consultant relationship and independent claims administrator is often the best path to capturing the greatest value from your health dollars.*

"Employees are our greatest asset" is a common expression, yet many companies don't operate that way. In highly competitive markets, leading employers are creating competitive advantages through innovative benefits plans built around high-value components that are often ignored or underutilized, such as primary care and mental health. This section gives you the new mindset and tools to do this reset.

CHAPTER 9

YOU RUN A HEALTH CARE BUSINESS WHETHER YOU LIKE IT OR NOT.

Here's How to Make It Thrive.

Warren Buffett said it all: "GM is a health and benefits company with an auto company attached." In fact, it spends more on health care than steel, just as Starbucks spends more on health care than coffee beans.

For most companies, health care is the second largest expense after payroll. This puts you in the health care business.

So, how's your health care business doing?

That's the first question the COO of a large private equity fund's health care benefits purchasing group asks when he sits down with the CEO of a newly acquired company, say a manufacturer. Naturally, the CEO will look puzzled. The COO will then show that the company has, for example, 4,200 members enrolled in their health plan and spends the typical $10,000 per year per member for health care. He then asks "How's your $42 million health care business?"

That's when the light bulb goes on, said the COO.

A Shift in Mindset

As we have seen, most companies don't apply the same level of care to their health care spending that they do to other large expenditures. Estimates of fraud, waste, and abuse in health care range from a low of 30 percent (Institute of Medicine) to over 50 percent (PwC) but are little known among employers.[95] Note that these are the same companies that often manage other major budget items down to the hundredths of a percent, yet accept annual 5 to 20 percent health care cost increases. In most cases, they have an overburdened, outgunned HR leader who is overseeing the health care spend with little or no analytic capabilities.

The reality is most companies wouldn't hire their present benefits leader to run a multimillion dollar million business unit or product. So why do they run a multimillion dollar benefits spend?

So, what's different about employers who are winning the battle to slay the health care cost beast? It's all about mindset. It's about waking up to the understanding that improving the value of health benefits is the best way to improve the well-being of their employees while boosting the company's bottom line—then committing to that path.

In virtually every case, the COO said, employers who have seen the light and taken action find their health care costs flatten or decline a bit while other employers continue to face ever-increasing health care costs. Soon, they're spending 20 percent less on health benefits per capita. Eventually, the most successful are spending 40-55 percent less. Plus, the financial and other advantages of waking up compound over time. As each year passes, the gap between wide-awake employers and those accepting the status quo grows.

As I've traveled to every corner of the country, I've seen wide-awake employers—large and small, rural and urban, public and private sector—who refuse to buy into what I believe has become the biggest lie in health care: that health care costs can't be controlled.

However, it's not just about costs. We've long heard CEOs state that employees are their most important asset. These wide-awake employers, from IBM to a small poultry processor in rural Wisconsin, have shifted their benefits mindset to match. Instead of looking at health benefits as a soft HR benefit, they now see them as investments in health and well-being that are strategic inputs to their supply chain and P&L. They manage health benefits programs accordingly.

Fair Trade for Health Care

In choosing care provider partners, wide-awake employers understand that the well-being of caregivers has a direct impact on the care of their employees. It's enlightened self-interest to make sure that physicians and other clinical staff are not abused by administrators, working conditions, compensation models, unbridled profit incentives, and other challenges that are sadly, very common. If the people running the show exhibit disdain for their own staff, how do you think they'll treat yours?

If you've ever bought Fair Trade coffee, you've probably done so in a deliberate effort to say no to products produced by child or slave labor, or whose owners run roughshod over the environment. I'm proposing that you likewise insist that health care organizations exhibit fair and ethical treatment of clinicians and patients before you become one of the latter. Here's what Fair Trade for health care should include.

- *Transparent prices.* Upfront pricing should be readily available without having to subscribe to a special service. Hospitals, physicians, and labs should have continued freedom to set their own prices, but predatory pricing, with a different rate for each person, is out of the question.

- *Bundled prices.* Imagine buying a car and getting a bill for the transmission six months later. You'd be livid, yet this sort of thing happens all the time in the health care industry. A transparent price must include the full bundle of services that wrap around it. This is the norm for the transparent medical markets we discuss later in this book. While not every last area of health care will fit into a bundle, it's broader than you might imagine. For example, the University of Oklahoma's Harold Hamm Diabetes Center has an all-in bundle for diabetes management (for different severity levels).

- *A culture of safety.* Given that preventable medical deaths are a leading cause of death in America and that medical errors bring untold misery to millions of patients every year, one of the best ways to identify a safe hospital is to ask nurses if they would want a family member to receive care in their facility and, if so, by which unit-level team. In fact, the Joint Commission (the U.S. accrediting body for hospitals) strongly recommends that hospitals measure safety culture, and most do, but this information is not shared with the public. Leapfrog Group safety scores is a great source for assessing this.

- *Staff treatment*: Physicians and nurses are suffering from record levels of suicide and burnout. To think this doesn't affect the quality of care they provide is naive. Research shows that patient outcomes are correlated with how a hospital treats its clinical staff.[96]

- *Ethics-based organizations.* There must be a focus on patient-reported outcomes. That is, patients want outcomes like living without pain or playing a sport—not just having a successful surgery, especially if it would have been better to avoid in the first place. Virginia Mason Hospital & Medical Center in Seattle, a forward-looking organization, has been candid in admitting that, at one time, 90 percent of its spinal procedures were of no help.[97]

While some worry about rationing care, the volume-driven reimbursement system has always rationed choices by pushing towards costly, invasive treatment options. Top-performing, value-based primary care organizations tell us that patients virtually always choose the least invasive treatment option first—but only if they're told about sound alternatives to expensive and overused treatments and tests. Equipping patients to become active partners in their own care is the sign of an ethical organization. So are ethical business practices, which definitely don't include intimidating doctors into relationships with a local hospital, an unfortunate common practice.

- *Data liquidity.* Care teams do their best work when they have the most complete view of a patient's health status. Anything less comes with an increased risk of harm. Likewise, your employees should have easy access to their own information in a secure, patient-controlled data repository—including the right to contribute their own data or take it elsewhere.

Two Stories

In the 2000s, IBM made a mindset shift about employee welfare and decided to integrate its health services. According to Paul Gundy, MD, and Martin Sepulveda, MD—the physicians who led these efforts—the company realized they were competing against giants like WiPro and Infosys from India, which have much lower cost structures. IBM would have to tackle the cost side of the equation, but they also saw that they could gain a strategic advantage if they had much higher-performing teams. Accordingly, they put a particular focus on the fitness, productivity, and resilience of their workforce.

Sepulveda explained to me their revelation that indiscriminate provision of health care services—absent efforts to help people understand how to use those services—leads to voracious appetites from both patients and health care providers for services that add little value but add a lot of cost to the individual, company, and society.

It dawned on him that if they were going to develop a worldwide health care strategy, they would have to build on universal values. People everywhere value health, access, receiving health care, and relationships in health care. It was striking to Sepulveda how important the relationship is between the person receiving care and the person delivering the care. What people understand and what they are willing to do is greatly influenced by that interaction. The ideal setting, he saw, is a full-function primary care setting that includes behavioral health and health coaching.

The challenge for a global leader like IBM was to develop a strategy that would work in vastly different environments: in rapid-growth countries with poor infrastructure, in a socialized country like France, and in a private insurance country like the U.S. They decided that, all other things being equal, they would put a third of their health care chips on prevention, a third on primary care, and a third on employee engagement with (and accountability for) their own health and with the health care system. The result is that IBM has built itself a competitive advantage with a lower cost structure and a higher-performing workforce.

On the other end of the spectrum with a very similar success story is Brakebush, a small poultry processor in rural Wisconsin with 1700 employees, many of whom are at high risk for injuries due to the nature of their job. For Brakebush, the wake-up call was a realization that they were pouring major resources into one of health care's most notorious money pits: musculoskeletal (MSK) procedures based on no scientific evidence, which in most cases provide less value than physical therapy (PT).[98]

They took a multipronged approach to eliminating the waste, including allocating resources to address and mitigate physical risks in their plants, hiring an onsite PT specialist to provide MSK care in a value-based fee model, and creating a new health care coordinator position to help employees navigate the health system. Brakebush now incentivizes employees who do need surgery to use designated centers of excellence for procedures that come with an upfront bundled price and warranty. They also use price transparency tools, a health care concierge, and health coaching. And in 2016, the company opened a health center that provides primary care, personal training, and a gym—at no cost to employees.

Sounds like a big investment, right? And yet Brakebush paid less for health care in 2016 than it did in 2014. It now spends 50 percent less than average for companies their size on MSK disorders, saving $1 million a year on just this one area.

What to Look For in a Health Plan Administrator

Obviously, you can't ask most HR benefits directors to pull off this kind of culture change. What you need is a sophisticated health administrator, analogous to the person who's administering your 401(k). This is someone whose skills and experience are commensurate with the magnitude of your investment in health benefits and the level of fiduciary responsibility it carries.

You want a person who is both numbers and people savvy, who understands the inner workings of a health plan, and who can bring real solutions to bear in a way that aligns the incentives of all parties. And then you want to give him or her the clout to get the job done with the respect and support of the C-suite. Depending on the size of your organization, this may be an outside advisor. This person must also be empowered with financial and other performance incentives that align with lowering costs and improving outcomes.

In short, you need someone able to run a major business, your health business. Here are some characteristics to look for.

- Outstanding finance skills with a focus on accuracy in forecasting and communicating stories through numbers

- Keen understanding that many types of cost-shifting to employees add financial stress that negatively impacts employee well-being and productivity
- Relentless focus on rooting out status quo health care industry practices designed to redistribute wealth and profits from you to them, including disclosure of commissions and fees, such as hidden bonus structures like insurance carrier overrides paid to benefits brokers
- Ability to understand and carry out ERISA and other fiduciary responsibilities for administering a high-performance health plan
- Insight into the moral impact and financial objectives of change and genuine concern for employees and their families
- Good communication skills
- Strong analytic, statistical, and actuarial skills to evaluate ROI in an industry that plays fast and loose with both promises and numbers
- Indefatigable learning, seeking proven solutions from any corner of the country / industry and innovative ideas that will disrupt the status quo
- Intimacy with the current state of affairs relating to health insurance and health care (i.e., not reliant on information spoon-fed by brokers)
- Ability to build consensus among influential peers, typically other employers and ideally those with large numbers of employees. By far, the greatest leverage is in numbers.

CHAPTER 10

HOW TO PICK A BENEFITS CONSULTANT

David Contorno

Recently, a Blue Cross plan offered brokers a $50,000 reward for switching self-insured clients back to more lucrative, fully-insured plans. In sectors like financial services, that kind of undisclosed conflict could land a person in jail. In health care, however, such clear conflicts of interest commonly exist and are often taken for granted.

For most companies, health care spending is one of the largest expenses on the P&L, often in the top two or three. However, few CEOs give it the resources, attention, or professional consulting they give other areas much farther down the list of expenses. Some businesses still leave benefits up to the HR department, which can lead to ill-informed decisions, however well intentioned, that are contrary to the company's (and often employees') best interests. While HR is critical when it comes to rolling out and administering the plan, financial decisions are best left to officers with financial backgrounds.

Knowing how to select a benefits advisor or consultant* who has the right skill set and experience in an industry that is often deliberately opaque can make all the difference in delivering true value to your employees.

How We Got Here

Some historical context is important here. In the '70s and '80s, when provider networks were first created, it was generally perceived as a very good thing for the industry and overall health care costs. For the first time, an insurance carrier could negotiate lower, predetermined prices and, in return, drive patients to the providers that agreed to accept these prices.

This allowed insurance carriers to differentiate through the discounts they negotiated with providers, a marketing message that continues to this day. Further, it allowed them to grow market share and, at least in some areas, drive health care financing costs. One thing that didn't change was paying brokers a commission on the premiums of the policies they sell, which dates back to the first life insurance policies sold in the 1800s.

Fast forward to 2010 and the passage of the Affordable Care Act (ACA). One provision, known as the Medical Loss Ratio requirement, was created with good intentions. The premise was that requiring carriers to spend a minimum of 80 to 85 percent of premiums (depending on plan type) on paying medical claims would prevent them from being overly profitable and would help control costs. It hasn't turned out this way for several reasons. First, after paying medical claims, broker commissions, and normal administrative costs, payers weren't making an unreasonable profit in the first place. In fact, it is a far smaller percentage of revenue than most businesses would be able to survive on, albeit a small percentage of a VERY large number.

Second, because profit is now tied to a percentage of premium, which is a function of underlying medical costs, the carrier now has an increased financial incentive to ignore increasing

---

*   *The more common term is broker and there are certainly some excellent brokers that do more than connect insurance carriers and employers, but the terms advisor or consultant speak to the need for a trusted partner who works closely with you to provide a broader range of services and better alignment with your interests. It reflects common usage in the self-insured market, but you should look more deeply than what someone calls themself.*

medical costs, so long as their costs don't rise any faster than those of competitors. This certainly existed before 2010 but the ACA turbo-charged the dynamic.

The common impression that insurance carriers' large networks and client pools gives them greater leverage in negotiating prices with providers could not be further from the truth. The more patients a hospital system treats from any particular carrier, the more leverage *the hospital system* has to increase fees. And employers unwittingly empower the provider's abuse by threatening to leave the carrier if they are unable to come to an agreement to keep that large local health care system in the network, even if it performs poorly.

For many years, all but the very largest employers have been fully invested in this arrangement. Brokers were paid a percentage of premium, employers deferred the entire responsibility for controlling costs to the insurance carrier, individuals consumed whatever care their clinician advised, and everybody was supposedly happy. But as underlying medical costs have gone up, the only winners are the insurance company, care providers (especially hospitals) and, of course, brokers.

A Broken Process

Here's what typically happens every year for those companies that are fully-insured. We will talk about how this works for self-insured companies shortly.

Around 60 days prior to the contract renewal date, your broker gets a renewal offer from the current carrier that has VERY little information explaining the proposed new premiums, which they can now use to shop around the market for a better offer. Note that this market is now tiny. Where there were 23 national health insurance carriers in 1990, there are now just four.

Let's pause for a moment to consider that the broker often gets no information at all if you have fewer than 100 employees. Even larger employers do not get full transparency, let alone proactive tools to address the underlying medical costs supposedly driving the new, higher rates. If your carrier released more data on your spending, their competitors would be able to "cherry pick" the money-making groups, weeding out the minority that lose them money every year.

Let's assume you are in that minority of money-losing clients. Why wouldn't your carrier just make an astronomically high renewal offer? They have to offer you something by law. They won't because if they actually want to get rid of you as a customer, an offer with too large an increase scares off all the other carriers—bringing them bad PR to boot.

Playing the Competition

Generally, carriers that want to win your business try to price their offer as high as they can while staying low enough to motivate you to move. That "motivation" used to be around a 10 percent premium increase, but with costs so high and employers accepting that switching carriers is just part of the game, the delta has shrunk significantly in recent years. Say your initial renewal offer from your current carrier is 18 percent. One of the other carriers believes you'll move for a 6 percent spread, so they offer a 12 percent increase over your current rates.

If your broker is loyal to a particular carrier—and they usually are, because the more clients they have with one carrier, the bigger their bonus income—he or she will share that 12 percent offer with their preferred carrier. Naturally, that carrier doesn't have to offer as much because you are already their customer, so maybe they match the new offer or come in at 1 percent above or below it.

Some brokers stop right there. They've shown their "value" by reducing the renewal rate by 6 percent, which can equal hundreds of thousands of dollars in some cases! Plus, you get to keep your current plan and stay with the "preferred" carrier in your state. Oh, and your broker gets a 12 percent pay raise for his efforts—and possibly additional bonus compensation.

Some brokers will send the 12 percent offer back to the other carrier, pitting the two carriers against each other and maybe squeezing out another few points. Either way, your rates are no longer about the cost of your employees' care. They are now about the carriers charging as much as they can and still keeping your business. Note that, in the unlikely event your broker were able to save you 20 percent on your premiums, he or she would also take a 20 percent cut.

The Bottom Line

Once the bottom-line number is reached, if the increase is still more than your budget can handle, the broker will then bring alternatives to reduce it that inevitably reduce benefits. One impact of reduced benefits has been a dramatic increase in employee out-of-pocket (OOP) costs in recent years, which has made the average worker afraid to even use their plan. Of course, this causes a delay in care until the person is much sicker, creating both a larger claim down the road and additional upward pressure on future rates.

One last trick to beware of: Brokers love to wait until the last minute to meet with you to review your upcoming plan renewal. Why? It may be that they are proverbially "fat and happy" and see no need to cater to your needs or perspective. It may be that they have bad news to deliver and prefer to delay tough conversations. Most likely they feel it will reduce your ability to talk with other brokers and perhaps make a change.

Why do so many brokers support this system? For one thing, it's all they've known. The average age of the typical broker is well into their 50s. For another, as premiums go up, so do their commissions, and carriers offer large bonuses to brokers when they both sell new business and keep the old business where it is. With few exceptions, most states allow for very large "incentive" compensation to brokers. This can mean lavish trips and, more important, as much as a 67 percent increase in pay over the percent paid for the same business to a less loyal broker.[99]

The Self-Insured Market

How does this translate to the self-insured market? Most consultants (although not all) that support self-insured plans are far more sophisticated than the brokers profiled earlier. If they're not, self-insured plans can be a financial disaster of epic proportions. Let's assume this is not the case. A consultant in this space needs to know (1) how to set up a plan and build it out component by component and (2) how to put protections in place for your company to ensure your liability is no greater than you can financially stomach. After all, now you're the insurer and "no lifetime cap" can be a scary proposition. However, a properly set up self-insured plan actually gives you far more control of costs than a fully-insured plan. With stop loss protection, it also lets you tailor your level of comfort with risk.

Here are the main components of high-performing self-insured plans.

- The third party administrator (TPA) that is responsible for paying claims (with your money) according to the specifications you set up and the supporting plan documents
- The network (usually "rented" from a large carrier) that provides discounts off billed charges
- Balance billing protection. Employers have a duty under ERISA to only pay fair and reasonable charges. After that price is determined and paid, some providers will try to get additional payment from an employee. A proper plan protects an employee against providers pursuing this. In extreme cases, that can include legal services for the employee.
- A pharmacy manager to handle the pharmacy network
- Pricing contracts
- Stop loss protection to pay for large claims

So now you are self-insured and are seeing a level of claims and spending detail you've never seen before. Yet costs are still going up each year at a similar rate or you saved some money the first couple of years. But now what? This is where the rubber meets the road for the more advanced consultant.

A common first misstep to lower costs is workplace wellness programs. As we saw in Chapter 8, at best, only a tiny percentage of such programs have a real ROI. At worst, they can cost a bunch more money, while irritating and potentially actually harming your employees. At least in the self-insured environment, you have access to data that can point you toward risk factors to focus on (or scuttle the entire program). But the initial excitement and enthusiasm of data access and your fancy new workplace wellness program quickly dies. Seventy-two per cent of companies have these programs and, I assure you, 72 percent of companies are not happy with their health care spending trends.

Instead, a progressive consultant brings you a multiyear health care plan designed to lower the quantity of care consumed, built on a proven approach to lower the actual cost of care for ALL employees—whether they are healthy or not.

The plan will generally reflect the following.

- Serious thought for ERISA fiduciary responsibility
- An emphasis on value-based primary care
- An emphasis on the highest-cost outlier patients
- Transparent medical markets/reference-based pricing (i.e. ways to know the actual prices you'll pay for services)
- Transparent pharmacy benefits
- Data proficiency

The plan will also include payment arrangements with providers and, importantly, complete disclosure of the consultant's sources of compensation.

Value Counts More Than Fees

However, none of this can take place if your company makes one very common mistake. You decide what consultant to use at the same time as you select your plans and other benefits for the upcoming year. The progressive consultant will help you see these as two distinct decisions that should be made at separate times.

As you can see, the actual "insurance" is a smaller and smaller piece of what the nontraditional benefits consultant brings to the table. In the self-insured model, stop-loss is the only insurance policy purchased, generally accounting for less than 20 percent of overall costs. This person should be able to provide you with all the information you need to identify the best renewal options for noninsurance administrative functions and, critically, the right strategies to positively impact both the cost and quality of your employees' care over the long term.

You don't necessarily want to pick your consultant based on how low their fee is. That doesn't speak to their true value. The fee is generally a small percentage—in the low single digits—of your total health care spend. This is how most businesses make that decision and we all know how well that's been working. A truly innovative consultant will be willing to put some of their compensation at risk, based on performance, and turn the commission conundrum described earlier on its head. Imagine paying your consultant a percentage of money actually saved! Now that's aligning incentives.

While no one expects a CEO to be an expert in all these areas, you should be generally aware enough to ensure that the people trusted with handling one of your largest expenses are.

One way you can judge a consultant's skill, integrity, and expertise is whether they're Health Rosetta certified. The certifications require transparency, expertise in key areas and strategies, and adherence to valid cost and outcome measurement models. Seasoned, high integrity professionals have already received this qualification. Learn more at healthrosetta.org/employers.

David Contorno is a benefit consultant helping midsize employers and is President of Lake Norman Benefits, a Member of the Hilb Group.

LANGDALE INDUSTRIES

Brian Klepper

L arge American businesses with tens or hundreds of thousands of employees have recruited high-profile benefits professionals to orchestrate sophisticated campaigns focused on the health of employees and their families, and on the cost-effectiveness of their programs. Even so, few large firms provide comprehensive, quality benefits at a cost that remains consistently below national averages.

For midsized businesses—firms with 100 to 5,000 employees—the task is significantly more difficult without the right people and focus. Health benefits managers in these companies have far fewer resources, typically work alone without the benefit of a large staff, and are often overwhelmed by the complexity of their tasks. As a result, they often default to whatever their broker and health plan suggest.

But a few excel. For them, managing the many different issues—chronic disease, patient engagement, physician self-referrals, specialist and inpatient overutilization, pharmacy management—is a discipline. Barbara Barrett is one of them.

Barrett is director of benefits at TLC Benefit Solutions, Inc., the benefits management arm of Valdosta, Georgia-based Langdale Industries, Inc., a small conglomerate of 24 firms and 1,000 employees. Langdale is engaged primarily in producing wood products for the building construction industry, but is also in car dealerships, energy, and other industries.

Valdosta is rural, which puts health benefits programs at a disadvantage. Often, as in this case, there is only one hospital nearby, which means little if any cost competition. Compared with those living in urban areas, rural Georgians are more likely to be less healthy and suffer from heart disease, obesity, diabetes, and cancer. So, the situation is far from ideal.

And yet, from 2000, when Barrett assumed responsibility for the management of Langdale's employee health benefits, to 2009, per employee costs rose from $5,400/year per employee to $6,072/year per employee in 2009. That's an average increase of 1.31 percent per year, compared to an average annual increase of 8.83 percent for comparably-sized firms nationally.[100] To put this in context, average firms spent $29 million more than Langdale from 2000 to 2009 to provide the same kind of coverage. Langdale's savings were $29,000 per employee—all without reducing the quality of benefits or transferring the cost burden to employees.

			Langdale Industries			
		Actual Premium* vs. US Trend and Cumulative Savings				
Year	US Trend**	Langdale (US Trend)	Langdale Actual***	Diff.	Diff. x 1,000 Eligible Emps.
2000		$5,400	$5,400		
2001	11.2%	$6,005	$5,741	$534	$534,060
2002	14.0%	$6,845	$5,542	$1,303	$1,303,065
2003	12.6%	$7,708	$5,615	$2,093	$2,093,989
2004	10.1%	$8,487	$5,689	$2,798	$2,798,941
2005	9.7%	$9,310	$5,763	$3,547	$3,547,612
2006	5.0%	$9,775	$5,839	$3,937	$3,937,601
2007	5.7%	$10,332	$5,915	$4,417	$4,417,301

2008	6.0%	$10,952	$5,993	$4,960	$4,960,756
2009	5.6%	$11,566	$6,071	$5,495	$5,495,583
Cumulative Savings $29,082,906					

For Medical, Dental, and Pharmacy
**Source - Kaiser/HRET 2009 Employer Health Benefits Annual Survey*
***Trended at an average of 1.31 percent between 2000 and 2009*

So how did Barrett approach the problem? Here are a few of her strategies.

- Langdale set up TLC Benefit Solutions, a HIPAA-compliant firm that administers and processes the company's medical, dental and drug claims. This allows Barrett to more directly track, manage, and control claim overpayments, waste, and abuse.
- It also gives her immediate access to quality and cost data on doctors, hospitals, and other vendors. Supplementing this data with external information, like Medicare cost reports for hospitals in the region, has allowed her to identify physicians and hospital services that provide low or high value. She has created incentives that steer individuals to high-value physicians and services and away from low-value ones. When necessary complex services are not available locally or have low quality or value, she shops the larger region, often sending patients as far away as Atlanta, three and a half hours by car.
- Barrett analyzes claims data to identify which individuals have chronic disease and which are likely to have a major acute event over the next year. Individuals with chronic diseases are directed into the company's evidence-based, opt-out disease management and prevention program. Individuals with acute care needs are connected with a physician for immediate intervention.
- Langdale provides employees and their families with confidential health advocate services that explain and encourage use of the company's benefits programs, again using targeted incentives to reward those who enter the programs and meet

evidence-based targets.

These are just a few of Barrett's initiatives in group health, but her responsibilities also extend to life, flex plan, supplemental benefits, retirement plan, workers' compensation, liability, and risk insurance. The results for Langdale in these areas include lower than average absenteeism, disability costs, and turnover costs.

The point isn't that you should just do what Barrett and Langdale have done. The point is that they've been proactive, endlessly innovative, and aggressive about managing the process. This attitude and rigor has paid off through tremendous savings, yes, but it has also produced a corporate culture that demonstrates the value of Langdale's employees and community. Employees and their families are healthier as a result and are more productive at work. This has borne unexpected fruit: The industries Langdale is in were hit particularly hard by the recession, and the benefits savings from Barrett's efforts helped save jobs.

Barbara Barrett and many others like her on the front line are virtually unknown in health care. Most often, their achievements go unnoticed beyond the executive offices. But they manage the health care and costs of populations in a way that all groups can be managed.

Editor's note: We checked in with Barbara recently and found that, even in the face of new challenges, such as extreme jumps in drug prices, Langdale continues to succeed where others have failed to carefully manage health costs.

Brian Klepper, PhD, is a health care analyst and principal of Worksite Health Advisors, based in Orange Park, Florida.

CHAPTER 11

THE 7 HABITS OF HIGHLY EFFECTIVE BENEFITS PROFESSIONALS

In previous chapters, I've highlighted tricks the status quo health care industry uses to redistribute profits from companies to their coffers. Here I will outline some basic antidotes that the most effective benefits leaders use to ensure their organizations don't needlessly overspend on health benefits.

Collectively, the approaches outlined below have enabled employers to sustainably save 20 percent or more on health benefits over the status quo.

Habit #1: Insist on Value-Based Primary Care

This is the bedrock of the highest-functioning health systems. Primary care providers own the patient relationship, are highly trusted by patients, and when properly incentivized, can be the first line of defense against downstream costs. Some of the characteristics of value-based primary care providers are the following.

- Are always available in one form or another
- Welcome and immediately address complaints
- Practice shared decision making with patients

- Adequately inform patients of the risks, costs, and invasiveness of all relevant treatment options
- Refer to specialists as a last resort and only to high value ones
- Integrates behavioral health and physical therapy into comprehensive primary care
- Close the loop when patients are seen by specialists or are admitted to inpatient care
- Are supported by nurse practitioners and physician assistants
- Offer care in convenient locations
- Offer direct contracted care arrangements that align their economic incentives with lowering costs and improving health outcomes

Habit #2: Proactively Manage Pharmacy Benefits

Successful Rx management has been described as playing whack-a-mole. Many pharmacy benefits management (PBM) firms are well known for hidden fees, shell game pricing, and taking drug manufacturers' money to promote specific drugs. You need to stay ahead of all of these tricks.

There are three pillars to effectively managing drug cost and quality.

1. Review PBM arrangements to determine the "spread" (PBM profit) and whether more favorable terms are available
2. Make formulary changes that have a large financial impact with next to no disruption
3. Carefully manage specialty drug purchase costs by shopping around

Habit #3: Have Specific Plans for Uncommon (But Predictable) Gargantuan Claims

You need a defined program for each common category of uncommon claims. It's not unusual for 6 percent of employees to account for 80 percent of total annual claim costs. They usually fall into these areas.

- **Dialysis** – With the rise of diabetes, this is inevitable. The best dialysis cost containment vendors offer multiple solutions aimed at setting the optimal price before treatment starts. They provide the most flexibility for choosing approaches that are appropriate to your specific situation.
- **Organ transplants, cancer, and complex surgery** – Sending beneficiaries to high-performance centers of excellence like Mayo Clinic and Virginia Mason Hospital & Medical Center will reduce unnecessary complications and procedures, saving enormous money despite travel costs.
- **Premature babies** – A comprehensive and closely monitored prenatal program is always worth it, especially if your employees have risk factors like advanced maternal age, diabetes, hypertension, and HIV.

Habit #4: Deploy Evidence-based Musculoskeletal (MSK) Management Programs

Given that MSK issues frequently account for 20 percent of claim costs and that over 50 percent of procedures are not evidence-based,[101] this is a tremendous opportunity to slash costs and ill-advised overtreatment. As we saw in Chapter 5, one manufacturer increased its earnings by 1.7 percent by getting just a third of employees' MSK cases into an evidence-based management program. The impact on the company's market cap was tens of millions of dollars.

Evidence-based approaches build on clinical knowledge with modern quality management techniques and data analytics. The results, validated in many settings, demonstrate far superior health outcomes.

Habit #5: Refuse to Sign Blank Checks to the Health Care Industry

Pricing failure is the most vexing problem in health care. True price transparency is the answer, e.g., bundled payments for the complete continuum of care for things like hip and knee replacements. You should demand nothing less. Virtually every area of the health care industry has high-integrity and high-quality providers that are happy to provide transparency. Find them and work with them. Health Rosetta will even help.

Habit #6: Protect Employees by Sending Them to Providers With First-rate Safety Records

In his book *Unaccountable*, Dr. Marty Makary, professor of surgery at Johns Hopkins, pointed out in devastating detail how flawed the safety culture is—and how hidden the failures are—in too many hospitals. No corporate travel department would allow an employee to fly on an airline that suppressed its safety records (even if the FAA allowed it). In the same way, it's unconscionable to blindly send an employee to a hospital with little or no information on its safety record. If the hospital suppresses that information, go elsewhere and tell your employees why.

Habit #7: Avoid Reckless Plan Document Language that Costs Millions

As mundane as ERISA plan language can sound, the most effective benefits leaders go over it with a fine-toothed comb. This is such an important topic that we've included sample document language in the Health Rosetta. You can read all about it in Chapter 19.

****

All your moves to implement these habits should be properly documented for two reasons. First, you want your entire team (not to mention your successor) on the same page. Second, not doing so can leave you and your company vulnerable to litigation related to health plan design and administration.

CHAPTER 12

CENTERS OF EXCELLENCE OFFER A GOLDEN OPPORTUNITY

Tom Emerick

As we have seen, there is a lot of unnecessary surgery and care performed in this country. This became a particular concern for me as a benefits manager in the 1980s when I was managing BP's self-insured U.S. health plans out of its Cleveland, Ohio office. I saw employees and their family members undergoing what seemed to me to be dubious procedures. This was not the case, so far as I could see, at the Cleveland Clinic, which was used by many BP plan enrollees. So, I set up a meeting with Cleveland Clinic executives to find out why.

Basically, they explained that their ethical standards prevented them from doing surgery on patients who did not need it. Furthermore, they had an evidence-based model for diagnosing patients with great accuracy and for prescribing the safest and least invasive effective solutions.

Clearly, steering our people their way was in our employees' best interests and would lead to better outcomes for our plan members and lower health care costs for BP.

What Is a Center of Excellence?

This is the definition of a center of excellence, a health care solution being adopted by savvy employers across the country today.

Hospitals and health centers that are the best at what they do, whether it's cardiac care, joint replacements, diagnostics, or something else.

A center of excellence typically offers the complete continuum of care for a chronic disease or acute condition such as diabetes or breast cancer, from diagnosis to treatment to rehabilitation—at lower costs than less capable providers.

These centers are fundamentally focused on patient care more so than on research or education, although they likely do both. They practice medicine using a team-based, data-driven, and accountable model. They perform high volumes of complex surgeries with great outcomes, yet they are more likely to recommend nonsurgical treatment plans whenever appropriate.

Employers that contract directly with centers of excellence are able to offer their plan members the best care at the best price. So that's what I did. I set up what was at that time the largest directly contracted preferred provider network in the United States. I put the Cleveland Clinic in as the primary referral center of excellence. And sure enough, surgery rates, almost across the board, dropped considerably.

Again, excellent diagnostics is a key to making this strategy work. Over the last 30 years, I have compiled data from various sources on patients who were sent to first-class referral centers for second opinions.

The following is a list of serious health conditions and the typical misdiagnosis rates.

- New cancer cases—20 percent
- Spine surgery—67 percent
- Orthopedic surgery—up to 30 percent

- Bypass surgery—60 percent
- Stents—50 percent in some parts of the US
- Solid organ transplants—40 percent

What to Look for in a Center of Excellence

Here are some of the traits that distinguish centers of excellence.

- Patients are seen by multiple specialists
- A multidisciplinary team does the diagnosis
- That same team prescribes the treatment plan
- If surgery is required, it is done at the highest quality available
- The patient experience is excellent
- Health care is integrated, collaborative, and accountable
- Bundled payments and global fees rather than fee-for-service payments

Health City in the Caymans Islands is emerging as possibly the best diagnostic and surgery center in the Western Hemisphere. A few other centers of excellence include Mayo Clinic in Minnesota, Virginia Mason in Washington, Mercy Hospital in Missouri, Intermountain Healthcare in Utah, Kaiser Permanente in California, Geisinger Health in Pennsylvania, and Baptist Health in Arkansas.

Remember that organizations are usually only a center of excellence for certain procedures and specialties, not everything.

The High Cost of Outliers

In health benefit plans today, about 6 to 8 percent of plan members are spending 80 percent of the plan dollars. Outliers may have wildly different medical conditions, but they have a lot in common.

- They tend to have complex health problems, usually with multiple comorbidities.
- They are often seeing three or four specialists, who rarely collaborate.
- In any given year about 20 percent of the outlier group is completely misdiagnosed. This means that about 16 percent of plan dollars each year are being wasted on treatments for diseases the patients don't have.
- About 40 percent of outliers have treatment plans that are flat out erroneous or clearly suboptimal. Adding this to misdiagnosis means that about 32 percent of total plan dollars each year are wasted, not to mention the huge amount of medical harm to the outlier population.
- Only a handful of outlier health problems are preventable in any real sense—about 7 percent, according to my colleague, Al Lewis. While the notion of workplace wellness and prevention was a noble idea, we now know that company after company is spending a huge amount of plan dollars and resources trying to do something that can't be done.

A senior executive at a Fortune 10 company wisely told me that misdiagnosis is the biggest health care error. Everything that follows both harms the patient and costs you. Again, a significant portion of outliers are misdiagnosed.

Those who succeed in controlling plan costs in the future will do so by focusing on outliers. One of the best solutions is using centers of excellence and taking advantage of superior referral centers to help ensure outliers are correctly diagnosed and given the optimal treatment plan.

In a typical center of excellence model, an employer pays the travel expenses for a patient and companion to travel to the center if it isn't local. If the patient needs surgery, he or she will have it at the center on the same trip. Even if the center is in another country, the quality of care more than makes up for the travel costs.

Getting Help

Admittedly, contracting directly with health systems that qualify to be centers of excellence usually takes a lot of effort, and you have to be a pretty large employer to get their attention. The good news is that "aggregators" are available today. These are specialty referral networks that can help companies with, say, less than 50,000 to 100,000 employees get prepackaged access to top-notch centers of excellence.

Some employers have expressed an interest in working with directly contracted centers of excellence, but have been unsuccessful in getting support from their brokers. There is growing evidence that some benefits firms have conflicts of interest in this arena, that is, they derive a large share of their total revenue by providing consulting services to specific providers. If a broker is getting 30 percent of their total revenue in this way, they may not want to help you send your patients somewhere else.

Is your broker in this category?

Tom Emerick is a consultant on health care benefits administration, founder of Edison Health, and coauthor of Cracking Health Costs and An Illustrated Guide to Personal Health. He previously led benefits programs at Walmart, BP, and elsewhere.

CHAPTER 13

INDEPENDENT CLAIMS ADMINISTRATORS VS. INSURANCE COMPANY CLAIMS ADMINISTRATORS –THE TRADE-OFFS

Adam V. Russo and Ron E. Peck

An increasing number of employers are looking to self-insure their employee health benefits for the first time. While this is a great first step toward better benefits and lower costs, it's important to realize that not all self-insuring is the same. It can vary enormously depending on whether you decide to work with an insurance carrier that provides the administrative services (ASO) or an independent third party administrator (TPA) that provides them.

First, let's nail down a few basic concepts. With fully-insured "traditional" insurance, your organization pays premiums to an insurance carrier and the carrier accepts the risk, meaning the carrier pays medical bills with its own funds. If the premiums exceed the medical expenses, the carrier "wins." If the medical expenses exceed the premiums, the carrier "loses." But for employers that can afford the risk—that have access to sufficient funds to pay the occasional midsized to large dollar claim—self-insuring has been shown to be less costly overall.

When a company self-insures its health plan, it sets aside its own money plus employee premiums, using them to pay claims for medical services itself. But rarely does an organization have the resources necessary to process claims—to receive, interpret, and pay medical bills. Nor does it understand the intricacies involved in creating and managing a health plan while complying with applicable laws. Thus an ASO or TPA is required.

Second, while most self-insured plans have adequate resources to pay most everyday medical expenses, few have enough to cover the cost of catastrophic claims resulting from care of patients with cancer, hemophilia, premature birth, etc. To address this, a self-insured plan will purchase reinsurance or excess coverage from a stop-loss carrier. This is not health insurance in the traditional sense. The stop-loss carrier does not pay medical bills, or deal directly with providers of health care. Instead, the self-insured plan—that is you, the employer—pays the medical bills. But once you have paid a certain amount (referred to as the specific deductible, attachment point, or "spec"), you can seek reimbursement from the stop-loss carrier.

Note: at various times in this discussion, we will refer to the employer as the *plan sponsor* or the *client*, but we always mean *you* the CEO and/or your company. Employees are also called *plan members*.

ASO and TPA at a Glance

The traditional and simplest way to administer a self-insured plan calls for a large insurance carrier to shed its risk-bearing role but continue to serve as a claims processor for the employer—substituting the employer's money for its own.

ASOs prefer to pick and hire the stop-loss coverage company (sometimes called excess or reinsurance coverage) for clients themselves and provide a predetermined health plan that aligns with its own excess loss carrier and provider network agreements. This bundling of the plan document, excess insurance, and network agreements severely limits plan customization. On the other hand, it eliminates potential gaps in coverage between these components.

The transition from a fully-insured health plan to a self-insured or partially self-insured plan is much easier with an ASO, because the insurer:

- Can continue to provide the same administration expertise it provided before, including the actuarial evaluation of how much money it will cost the employer to fund its own program
- Can provide other professional services such as accounting, legal advice, expert medical opinions, and regulatory compliance
- Is usually familiar with the medical providers known to the employees and their health risks, both important to handling claims

The downside is that the employer can't take as much of an active role in cost management or provider relations. Nor can it easily negotiate a direct contract with a hospital or "carve out" a particular type of claim. In return for one-stop shopping, you generally do what the ASO dictates, limiting flexibility to significantly reduce spending.

With a TPA, on the other hand, you call the shots and get more transparency and flexibility at what is generally a lower cost. The TPA does what you dictate.

As benefit plans have become more sophisticated and self-insuring more popular, we've seen a nationwide proliferation of increasingly professional TPAs. These independent administrators offer a broad range of services. At one end, is the simple administration of benefit payments. At the other, is a "turn-key" contract that includes a stop-loss provision like an ASO but is still more flexible and affordable.

Due to consolidation, there are fewer small "boutique" TPAs these days, but even the larger TPAs dominating the market still maintain more of a customized approach than an ASO. They are more flexible, more likely to be local, and offer employers the opportunity to access claims data. They also let you pick and choose vendors and providers to meet your specific usage needs. Thanks to their highly specialized products and lower overhead, TPAs have developed pricing strategies that make them cost-effective. A TPA can afford medical expertise and achieve group purchasing discounts that are significantly more advantageous than those available to a single employer.

More employers are finding that it's worth risking potential gaps in coverage with a TPA, in exchange for being able to shop around and field offers from various stop-loss carriers. Also, ASOs are generally proprietary about claims data. If you as the employer want to know if your smoking cessation program has yielded an ROI, it can be hard to get data. If you want to examine your costs for diabetes treatment before deciding on a program for Type 2 diabetics, it can be hard to get data. With a TPA, you have complete access to the data, allowing you to design your plan accordingly. Increasingly, employers believe it's unconscionable to not have visibility into what is likely their organization's biggest expenditure after payroll.

Here's another difference. Many self-insured plans place great emphasis on their preferred provider organization (PPO). (See Chapter 6 for more on PPOs and how they are responsible for keeping health costs so high.) This is a prearranged network of providers that agree to treat plan members for a discounted rate and to accept that amount as payment in full. The biggest, most effective networks are owned and managed by large insurance carriers, but provide the best network access to their own insurance programs and ASO plans. While it is true that many TPAs "rent" networks from these carriers, the carriers do not provide their deepest discounts to anyone outside their organization.

That being said, some TPAs are forgoing the "national network" approach, instead focusing on direct contracting with individual providers for even better rates, and/or forming narrow networks of select providers for rates that rival or beat the best national PPOs. The downside, of course, is that if plan members go outside the narrow network for treatment, they can be billed out of pocket for the balance after the plan pays the maximum amount allowable according to the contract—something that doesn't happen if the plan and provider are part of a national PPO.

With a TPA, there is a true unbundling of services. For some employers, the fact that a TPA requires the employer to see and select the moving parts is exciting. It allows a hands-on employer to more actively contain costs and pick what they feel is best for their employees. For others, it is frightening and overwhelming. For those employers, an ASO that makes the decisions for them is likely the way to go—if they're willing to pay the premium.

ASO Benefits

There are a lot of parts to administering a benefits plan and an ASO will take care of all of them.

- Accounting and recordkeeping
- Plan design
- Actuarial analysis
- Underwriting
- Securing stop-loss coverage
- Investment advice
- Enrollment
- Utilization review
- Medical record audits
- Plan booklet preparation
- COBRA administration
- Plan communication
- Reporting and disclosure
- Contribution determination
- Claims administration
- Statistical analysis
- Subrogation
- Claim appeals
- Record retention

The ASO will also decide whether, when, and how much to pay for claims.

Of late, insurance carriers, including their ASO arms, have improved their service capabilities, making them more transparent. In some cases, it is possible for a self-insured employer to log onto an ASO's technology platform and instantly receive claims status reports—for an extra cost, mind you.

As self-insuring has become more important in the market, some insurance carriers also have implemented programs to make their products easier to use. This revolution in customer service includes onsite processing personnel, 800 numbers, artificial intelligence systems, image processing, and other advanced technology designed to generate one-call responses to member inquiries.

Self-insuring with an ASO is truly a turn-key solution. You and your employees enjoy a seamless transition from fully-insured traditional insurance. There are no gaps between the plan's coverage and stop-loss coverage. Yet there is a cost for this all-in-one approach. In addition to administrative fees that admittedly range but almost always exceed the fees charged by TPAs (sometimes doubling them), your rights to examine data and customize your plan, as well as pick and choose stop-loss carriers and vendors, is limited, and stop-loss insurance premiums are usually greater. Together, these conveniences , along with bundled pharmacy services, significantly limit your ability to proactively and significantly reduce your total spending.

TPA Benefits

Different types of TPAs have different strengths. On large accounts, for example, the large nationwide TPAs can compete favorably with large insurers' ASO-driven products. Smaller, local TPAs can generally respond more quickly to plan changes than their larger counterparts.

Interacting and working with a TPA on a local level can bring a high degree of control to the administrative process. A TPA located in the same community as an employer has the advantages of knowing the market, employees, providers, and general economic conditions. This familiarity can lead to administrative and benefits efficiencies. If the TPA is part of a local managed care organization, serving other employers, it has a stronger negotiating position.

A thorough knowledge and understanding of the labor market and the benefits available locally for various employee classifications will also help in planning benefits. This means they will be competitive and likely to achieve the goals of the employers' overall benefit strategy.

Two other advantages that TPAs have over ASOs are negotiating "in network" claims and changing terms in the summary plan description (SPD). Because many ASOs are affiliated with the PPO network they use (often sharing a parent company or other affiliation), they are typically expected to process all in-network claims quickly—without examining them. While quick and painless claims payments certainly limit conflicts with providers and insured individuals, they also make it more likely that excessive charges, duplicate and fraudulent claims, and other billing errors will be missed.

Recently, a TPA processing claims for its self-insured plan client performed an audit on in-network claims (something an ASO might not be allowed to do) and discovered a $3.6 million claim *after* the network discount. The claim featured many coding and other mistakes, but once these were addressed, the final payment was a much more manageable $1.6 million!

Whether because the claims processing system is keyed to work with a particular benefit plan template, or because applicable network and stop-loss policies are written in concert with the plan document, many ASO-managed plans are stuck with a predetermined SPD document. For many self-insured employers, this is a great comfort. For others, the lack of discretionary authority is troublesome. In one case, an employer working with an ASO was strongly opposed to paying for claims arising from any and all illegal acts. The plan document excluded only claims arising from felonies. When the employer asked to expand the scope to all illegal acts, he was told that such a change would disrupt coordination with the claims system, stop-loss, and network contracts.

As cost containment and managed care become increasingly important, the balance is tipping toward the TPA alternative.

Another Consideration:
Are You Hiring an Independent Advocate?

Whether ASO or TPA, some claims processors are partly owned by large insurance carriers, health systems, network administrators, and other entities. This means that when you want to dispute something with one of those entities, their claims processor may need to bow out due to a conflict of interest. In one instance, a small employer's plan members were being asked by a local hospital to pay a portion of their bill *up front* because the plan didn't use a recognized provider network. The hospital was not hassling members of other, much larger area employer plans administered by the same TPA and likewise not using a network. The TPA confronted the hospital on the plan's behalf, leveraging the weight of all of its clients, to force the hospital to explain the issues and devise a better solution. Had the TPA been beholden to the hospital, this wouldn't have happened.

In another instance, the employer sponsoring a self-insured plan was questioning a hospital's billing practices. When it refused to pay the full billed charges, the hospital returned the plan's partial payment, threatening to "balance bill" the individual directly for 100 percent of the billed charges. Had the plan been working with a TPA or ASO that was affiliated with the hospital, it almost certainly would have pushed the employer to reissue payment in accordance with the network terms.

Because the TPA was entirely independent, it agreed to issue the plan's maximum allowable payment directly to the individual. In addition, it hired an advocate to represent the individual in negotiating with the hospital. By taking these steps, the individual, employer, and TPA were able to get the provider to abandon a 2 percent discount in favor of a 35 percent discount, saving almost $30,000.

A Closer Look at Fiduciary Responsibility

One benefit inherent in an ASO approach relates to fiduciary duties. A self-insured employer, unlike an employer purchasing a fully-insured health plan, is deemed to be a fiduciary of the plan members. This means he or she is legally bound to act prudently and only in their interest. Actions that are deemed to be in error, arbitrary, or capricious can expose employers to treble damages, that is, penalties are sometimes equal to three times the damage caused. For many employers, who have never taken on a fiduciary role, this is intimidating and not welcome. More often than not, an ASO is willing to take on that role with you.

With TPAs, things are less straightforward. A TPA is a contract service provider, not a plan administrator. The administrator role is reserved for the employer or trustee-appointed fiduciary. However, TPAs increasingly are taking on plan administrator functions—and with them, apparently, increased liability.

For example, TPAs are promoting programs such as Multiple Employer Welfare Arrangements or "MEWAs," which are statutorily regulated plans comprised of multiple smaller employers banding together to form a plan, moving into marketing, stop-loss procurement, and consulting services. In response, TPAs are coming under scrutiny for their handling of plan funds and invested assets. Courts already have found some traditional claims administration functions to be of a fiduciary nature—particularly in regard to handling and management of plan assets—and have held TPAs accountable under the higher standards of conduct as functional fiduciaries.

Some states have attempted to regulate TPA services as a form of insurance business. However, a number of courts have held that state regulation of TPAs—and of self-insured plans—is preempted by ERISA (the Employee Retirement Income Security Act of 1974).

Even if you hand over fiduciary duties to a TPA or ASO, ERISA says you may remain liable for its breach of its duties *if*, say, there are no procedures in the plan to delegate those duties. But if there are procedures and you follow them, you will be held responsible for the TPA's misconduct *only if you failed to exercise prudence in selecting the TPA or monitoring their performance.*

Naturally, you will want to consult an attorney in this matter.

Ready to Get Started?
A Checklist for Decision Makers

Here are some reasons you might decide to self-insure.

1. **Plan control.** You choose what to cover and exclude. With a TPA, you are able to directly control costs by designing and implementing care strategies that are informed by your culture, employee behaviors, and local health and provider resources.
2. **Interest and cash flow.** Funds are in your hands until they're needed.
3. **Federal preemption and lower taxes.** ERISA states that a private, self-insured health plan isn't subject to conflicting state health insurance regulations.
4. **Data access.** You can, if you have a TPA, examine claims data, study trends, allocate resources, and form partnerships to address your company's unique needs.
5. **Risk reduction.** Reducing risk and costs directly impacts you and your employees, plus you're unaffected by other populations.

On the other hand, you and your employees are used to a fully-insured traditional insurance policy, with all that implies:

"in-network" access to providers, often nationwide; knowing those providers will accept whatever the plan dictates in terms of charges; predetermined decisions about what is covered and what is not, and how a complicated claim should be handled.

How important are these things to you?

Take some time to consider the following before making your decision to self-insure pick either a TPA or an ASO.

- Do you want to make the effort to compare your plan document, which you helped draft, to a stop-loss carrier's policy to be sure you won't be stuck paying certain types of claims the carrier doesn't cover? Or, would you rather someone else handle drafting the plan and picking stop-loss?
- Do you care whether you have a nationwide network or do you prefer local narrow networks and direct contracts, which might save you more money, but expose your employees to the possibility of balance billing?
- Do you care who services your plan—who's watching the claims and who's making sure your plan is being reimbursed when someone else is supposed to pay?
- Do you care whether you're paying for services and programs your employees don't actually need or use? Are you concerned your population has needs not being adequately addressed?
- Do you want to implement the most innovative, evidence-based practices to improve employee health and reduce waste and costs?

If you place more importance on a large network, steep discounts (albeit off of inflated prices you've never seen and over which there are no controls), and avoiding decision making (and liability for those decisions), then you are an ideal candidate to self-insure with an ASO.

If you are willing to risk potential gaps in coverage between your plan and your stop-loss and assume liability for decision making as a fiduciary, in exchange for controlling which providers your employees have access to, what your plan covers, and which programs, vendors, and carriers you work with, then you are a prime candidate for self-insuring with a TPA.

Ron E. Peck, Esq. is senior vice president and general counsel and Adam V. Russo, Esq. is the cofounder and chief executive officer of The Phia Group, an organization dedicated to empowering health plans' ability to maximize benefits while minimizing costs.

What to look for in a TPA

Is the TPA able to drive you value? This can be in the following forms.

- Value-based contracting
- Integration with local primary care practices
- Chronic care management and reporting
- Cost and quality transparency
- Seamless integration and promotion of third-party solutions like telehealth or second opinions
- Flexibility in customer communication (phone only between 8am and 5pm? Or text, email, chat anytime?)

Will the TPA be able to smoothly accommodate you as a new client? One clue is the size of your company relative to the TPA's other clients.

What is the TPA's performance track record on things like turn-around time for claims processing (seven to 10 business days is average) and accuracy (look for a percentage in the upper 90s)? Reputation in the stop-loss market is a good indicator.

What do their turnover rate, past performance evaluations, reference checks, feedback from dissatisfied clients, and pending litigation tell you about the performance of individual staff who will administer your program?

Is the TPA's technology sophisticated enough to account for and appropriately allocate the cost of benefits, provide a superior customer experience, evaluate the cost of the various benefits being offered, and the efficiencies of providers? (In many cases, the answer is no.)

Does the TPA have a strong relationship with a stop-loss carrier that might help sway excess coverage reimbursements in your favor?

Is the TPA able to meet the competing demands of federal privacy rules and Department of Labor claims procedures rules that accelerate the decision-making process? Can it meet HIPAA's standardization requirements for electronic codes and formats?

Is the TPA prepared in terms of technological capabilities and capital resources to operate in the ever-more demanding compliance environment?

Part IV

Health Rosetta

*T*his is the how-to portion of the book. The Health Rosetta blue-print represents the work of the best minds in health benefits and the employers that have had many years of sustained success follow-ing their lead. This section lets you contrast what your current benefits plans with proven best-practice approaches. The Health Rosetta evolves nearly every day as evidence and ideas are shared in this open source community. Like the Rosetta Stone, the Health Rosetta is the path to deciphering health care's hieroglyphics.

For example, every employer who has slayed the health care cost beast has recognized the importance of proper primary care. Sadly, most Americans experience a badly undermined primary care model that is largely a referral machine to costly and often unnecessary treatments.

A very small portion of your employees in a given year account for a large percentage of your health care spending. It's not uncommon for 6 percent of your employees to account for 80 percent of your spending. Unfortunately, up to 50 percent of these high cost and complex cases are riddled with misdiagnoses and inappropriate treatment, which inevita-bly lead to worse outcomes and higher costs.

We wrap up with a checklist of necessary elements to include in an ERISA health plan that will protect and empower your organization.

CHAPTER 14

VALUE-BASED PRIMARY CARE

What is Value-based Primary Care?

Value-based primary care (VBPC) is an umbrella term that includes various delivery models that involve direct financial relationships between individuals or employers and primary care practitioners (PCPs) *outside* of the traditional fee-for-service insurance model, though your plan administrator may manage the value-based contract rather than you directly. Value-based primary care offers patients, physicians, and purchasers an alternative to traditional fee-for-service (FFS) payment arrangements, in which physicians are reimbursed according to the volume of services they provide regardless of quality. VBPC has matured as health care purchasing shifts from volume to value payment models.

Value is defined as the ratio of quality to cost. Value increases as the quality of the care increases or the cost of care decreases.

In the United States, there are two primary models for VBPC, though this space is evolving rapidly with much more differentiation emerging.

- Direct primary care (DPC), in which care is offered directly to individuals, plan administrators, and employer in a range of practice models from solo practitioners to national organizations

- Onsite/near-site clinics fully or partially dedicated to the workforce of a specific employer

How Does It Work?

Providers of VBPC typically charge a monthly, quarterly, or annual membership fee, which covers all or most primary care services including acute and preventive care. The fee is paid out of an individual's own pocket, by a sponsoring organization such as an employer or union, or by a health plan offering commercial or government programs, such as a Medicare Advantage plan. Most commonly, the practice has been devoted to the particular sponsoring entity (e.g., a near-site clinic for employers/unions or a Medicare Advantage-based clinic devoted to seniors), but models that serve multiple clients are maturing.

The flawed incentive structure of FFS demands very short primary care appointments, which often drive referrals to unnecessary high-margin services such as scans and specialists and result in an overreliance on prescriptions. The reduced overhead from eliminating FFS billing also allows VBPC practices to offer a more proactive care model that can lead to significant reductions in downstream costs.

Why Should You Support It?

VBPC aligns your interests with primary care providers, which can improve health outcomes and significantly lower costs for your employees and members. Health outcomes are improved by shifting the focus from reactive, episodic care to a continuous care relationship, population health strategies such as preventive and chronic care, optimizing specialty care referral channels, and care management.

The VBPC model also delivers a substantially better experience for patients, often in one or more of the following ways.

- More time with their provider
- Same day appointments
- Short or no wait times in the office
- Better technology, e.g., email, texting, video chats, and other digital-based interactions
- 24/7 coverage by a professional with access to their electronic health record
- Far more coordinated care

VBPC also improves provider experience and professional satisfaction, which, in turn, is known to improve the quality of care.

What Are the Key Elements to Look For in a VBPC Provider?

1. Quality Reporting

Clinical quality measures (e.g., What percentage of patients were vaccinated in line with standard schedules? Required hospitalization? Received domestic violence screening?) are reported in appropriate detail to:

- The individual patient
- The purchaser
- A community health information exchange (HIE), where available

2. Shared Decision-making

PCPs use established communication techniques to ensure patients are educated and engaged in making decisions about their own care, being respectful of preferences, ethics, and economic concerns. Coordinating efforts with employers and health plans, PCPs clarify and validate health information about patient conditions, rights, and available options.

3. Care Coordination

PCPs actively coordinate care with specialists and ancillary providers, ensuring post-hospital and post-surgical follow-up. Care coordination should not be predicated or dependent on all providers sharing a common electronic health record (EHR). Employers and plans should exert leverage on all nonconnected providers to share information via an HIE.

4. Population Health Management

Management of chronic conditions is proactive, aggressive, and team-based, using patient advocates, care manager nurses, and personal health assistants/coaches. Care is facilitated through the use of patient registries, either embedded in the EHR or through collaboration with the HIE.

Preventive services include evidence-based screenings (specifically excluding those known to be harmful or of questionable value) and active pursuit of both childhood and adult vaccinations according to current recommendations from the Advisory Committee on Immunization Practices of the Centers for Disease Control and Prevention.

5. Value-based Payment Models

Compensation models reward physicians on a nonvolume basis, such as straight salary, per member per month fees, or the overall number of patients for which they are responsible. Purchasers should look for a portion of VBPC provider compensation being dependent on value, as determined by some combination of quality metrics, patient experience scores, and resource stewardship. The general nature of the compensation model should be transparent to help inform the purchaser's selection of providers.

6. Patient Experience

Standard methods are used to measure patient experience and engagement. Patient advisory panels are incorporated in the practice to offer guidance about service functions and assure a patient-centered orientation. Purchasers should expect to see aggregated experience scores as one measure of quality.

7. Evidence-based Medical Care

The practice is grounded in evidence-based medicine—as demonstrated to purchasers through transparency of clinical process and outcomes measures, as well as provider education and collaboration—that respects patients' insurance coverage or financial status, personal preferences, and ethics.

8. Participation in a Health Information Exchange (HIE)

The practice shares data with specialists, other providers including hospitals, and other relevant parties through participation in an HIE as a regular part of care that is incorporated into appropriate workflows.

9. Ease of Access to Care and Care Information

A patient portal is available to access personal health records and facilitate asynchronous communication between patients and providers. A patient is not expected to make an office visit unless physical presence is necessary for quality of care. The practice collects data on standard access metrics and shares them with a patient advisory panel and the health care purchaser, and provides complaint resolution and follow-up. Patients have 24/7 telephone access to a health care professional with immediate access to the patient's EHR and a physician or advanced practitioner backup, thus reducing unnecessary ER use.

10. Clinical Pharmacy and Mental Health Embedded within Practice

The practice provides clinical pharmacy support for patients with complicated drug regimens and those requiring additional support for drug-related concerns, including resources to help patients unable to afford prescribed pharmaceutical treatments. Mental health services for common issues (typically depression and anxiety) that can be managed on an ambulatory basis are readily and conveniently available through the primary care office.

11. Physician Loyalty

At all times and in all matters, including testing, referrals, hospitalizations, and all care outside the office, the physician and other providers in the PCP practice align with the patient's care interests and personal economics. Physicians strive to deliver the highest quality at the most reasonable cost and put patient interests above others.

12. Referral Patterns

VBPC clinics should take an active role in referring patients to high value specialists and facilities.

What Challenges Can You Expect?

1. Administrative Challenges

Your broker, consultant, carrier, or TPA may be unable or unwilling to help you evaluate the appropriateness of VBPC for your health plan.

2. Employee Education

Employees in established primary care practices may be unwilling to switch to one using a VBPC model—at least initially. Inertia, comfort with current providers, and lack of awareness of their current care quality are all impediments. Being able to demonstrate both financial and nonfinancial benefits to them is key, as is making clear that they are not being forced to see a "company doctor." The need for frequent, clear communication with employees and dependents can't be overemphasized.

3. Care Dislocation

Having large numbers of people switch primary care physicians can be challenging, especially when physicians in the receiving practice may be overwhelmed by the sudden increase in a short period. Talk with the new physicians to understand their capacity and access issues. Don't wait for your employees and their families to complain.

4. Criteria for Choosing a Practice

Practices may market themselves as low-cost providers, but primary care should never be purchased solely on cost. Expect to spend more on high-quality primary care in return for downstream savings and other benefits (e.g., increased productivity and employee satisfaction) that will more than cover the increased costs. Choose primary care based on patient service, demonstrated clinical quality metrics, and demonstrated attention to stewardship of your dollar.

5. Care Coordination

Current providers and health systems may warn that VBPC encourages care fragmentation and loss of coordination, no longer a tenable argument in today's digital age. Insist on the adoption of a health information exchange and other technology to overcome this barrier.

6. Slow Migration to the New VBPC Model

People are much more willing to change PCPs when they get to meet the doctor beforehand. If possible, arrange for your new PCPs to visit with employees at your workplace. Also, arrange tours of the new practice location. Employers willing to provide strong incentives to try out the new primary care model will achieve much higher adoption rates.

7. Obfuscation to Preserve Status Quo

Physicians who aren't forward-looking may fall back on "fear, uncertainty, and doubt" tactics meant to freeze progress. As stewards of your organizations' and employees' hard-earned money, you must choose whether to protect your own bottom line or that of your vendor.

What Action Steps Can You Take?

Ask your broker, consultant, insurance carrier, or TPA if they are currently working with or have experience with VBPC practices.

Encourage your broker, consultant, carrier, or TPA to find, interpret, and share reliable cost and quality data from primary care groups competing for your business.

Consider comparing primary care groups through a structured and disciplined RFP process. Also consider modifying your benefits plan to provide incentives for employees and their families to try a VBPC practice.

Visit a local VBPC practice and see for yourself.

Additional Resources

Please visit healthrosetta.org/health-rosetta for ongoing updates, including lists of value-based primary care organizations, case studies, best practices, toolkits, and more.

CHAPTER 15

TRANSPARENT MEDICAL MARKETS

What is a Transparent Medical Market?

A transparent medical market (TMM) offers purchasers such as employers and unions fair and fully transparent pricing for medical services/procedures ranging from specific treatments (e.g., knee replacement or colonoscopies) to specific conditions (e.g., diabetes or kidney disease). Services and procedures are typically bundled, meaning there is just one bill for all the services received for a specific treatment or condition that includes multiple providers and sometimes multiple settings. Another dimension of transparency is that the market is open to any provider who has sufficiently high-quality indicators and charges fair prices.

A TMM offers employers an alternative to traditional fee-for-service (FFS) payment models, in which individual services are listed on itemized billing statements from multiple sources.

How Does It Work?

Providers (typically independent imaging centers, specialty hospitals, and ambulatory surgery centers) supply up-front pricing at significantly reduced rates in exchange for increased volume, quick pay, reduced friction, and avoiding claims/collections problems—all factors that allow providers to charge greatly reduced prices while netting a similar amount to standard insurance billing.

Providers contract directly with an employer or third party to offer services outside of a typical payment and network structure. In exchange for significantly reduced rates, employers encourage plan members to use these providers, typically by waiving all of the individual's costs including copays, coinsurance, and deductibles.

Why Should You Support It?

Unlike FFS, which allows for wildly variable, opaque pricing free from market forces and that can incentivize providers to offer unnecessary services, TMM benefits providers, employers, and employees. Providers get access to individuals whose employers offer quick pay and reduced hassles, while employers get access to bundled, transparent rates at prices typically 30 to 50 percent lower than typical *network* discount prices (and even more off of chargemaster prices). Employees get access to a new benefit that offers medical services and procedures without financial penalties in the form of copays and deductibles. In short, providers get easier administration and certainty, employers get great prices, and patients get the care they need at no additional cost.

What Are the Key Elements to Look for?

1. Transparency

It's not possible for employers to measure the value of their health care dollar without access to pricing and quality information. The same information is needed by employees if they are expected to seek high-value care. At a minimum, all medical services and procedures should be available at fair, honest, and up-front prices, making health care services as straightforward as other products and services we buy. Quality information should also be readily available for employers and employees alike.

2. Bundled Payment

Bundled payment for a specific treatment allows employers to trade endless, confusing, itemized bills for just one bill covering the hospital, surgeon, anesthesia, equipment, etc. For treatment across a specific condition there is just one bill for all physician visits, diagnostics, and care management.

3. Shared Risk

Medicare has long required providers to share risk under three different "global" periods (zero-day postoperative, 10-day postoperative, and 90-day postoperative) by refusing to pay for mistakes, complications, and re-admissions. A TMM brings that practice to private health plans.

4. Efficient Administration

Typical claims administration is filled with inefficiencies: slow payment cycles, prior authorization, network requirements, complicated payment models, employee cost sharing, etc. For a TMM to work, employers must make it easy for employees to access care, offer quick pay to providers (typically five days or less), eliminate barriers like copays and deductibles, and often remove oversight requirements like prior authorization. It's important to remember that the goal of this model is to simultaneously lower employer costs, reduce costs and eliminate hassles for providers, and provide a true benefit to employees and members.

5. Employee Education

Models that encourage the use of specific providers for specific treatments are often a new idea for employees and their families. They need to understand that TMM is *not* like HMO models, which were often associated with denied care, long wait times, and poor customer service. The message needs to be simple, clear, intriguing, and just one sentence like this: *Don't forget, if you need medical care, we have a group of the highest-quality providers you can see, and choosing this won't cost you anything out of pocket.*

6. Ease of Use

Health care has always been confusing, frustrating, and very often scary. A TMM should be effortless. Consider offering concierge-style customer service, which gives your employees easy access to the humans and resources they need, including hassle-free appointment scheduling, medical records transfer, and both web and mobile access. These services can also create comfort for your employees around sensitive health issues they don't want to discuss with you or your internal benefits manager.

How Can You Ensure Quality?

An effective TMM functions best in tandem with a value-based primary care model and use of shared decision-making tools to avoid overtreatment and radiation exposure from unnecessary scans. Any high-quality provider should be participating in all applicable quality reporting whether they are a health system, ambulatory surgery center, imaging center, or independent physician practice. Here are some resources that can help ensure that the providers you use are, in fact, of the highest quality.

- *HealthInsight* is a private, nonprofit, community-based organization dedicated to improving health and health care. They offer a free ranking tool for hospitals nationwide.
- *The National Quality Forum* (NQF) is a nonprofit, nonpartisan, membership-based organization that works to catalyze improvements in health care. They offer access to a huge library of evidence-based quality measures.

- *Hospital Compare* is a government website that allows you to find and compare quality information for more than 4,000 Medicare-certified hospitals across the country.
- *The Leapfrog Hospital Survey* is the gold standard for comparing hospitals' performance on national, professionally endorsed standards of safety, quality, and efficiency that are most relevant to consumers and purchasers of care.

What Challenges Can You Expect?

1. Administrative Challenges

Your broker, consultant, carrier, or TPA may be unable or unwilling to provide transparent specialty care and the administration to execute a TMM.

2. Provider Reluctance

It is common for the large health systems you currently use to push back on requests for price and quality transparency.

3. Complex Implementation

The process can be quite cumbersome and drawn out should you decide to go it alone. You might consider using a third party to help streamline the process.

4. Employee Education

TMM models require continued messaging and clear, easy-to-understand action steps.

5. Data Sharing

It could be difficult to obtain pricing and quality information from your current broker, consultant, carrier, or TPA. Since it is your spend, you have a right to this information.

6. Data Analytics

Traditional claims analysis software programs and services are often limited in scope and not designed to provide clarity or actionable insight.

7. Confusion about Price Transparency Tools

Many price transparency tools (e.g., Castlight) provide information on insurance PPO network pricing, but they don't remove the hassles and costs for either providers or individuals related to claims, copays, etc.

8. Obfuscation to Preserve Status Quo

Your current providers who aren't forward-looking are likely to use common "fear, uncertainty, and doubt" tactics meant to freeze progress.

As stewards of your organizations' and employees' hard-earned money, you must choose whether to protect yours our your vendor's bottom line.

What Action Steps Can You Take?

Ask your broker, consultant, carrier or TPA if they participate in any transparency initiatives.

Encourage your broker, consultant, carrier, or TPA to make cost and quality data available to both you and your employees.

Consider modifying your benefits plan to provide incentives for employees and their families to access care from transparent providers.

Visit a local hospital or surgery center to discuss or consider tapping a third-party TMM vendor in your region or may expand to serve your employees.

Additional Resources

Please go to healthrosetta.org/health-rosetta for ongoing updates, including lists of TMM organizations, case studies, best practices, toolkits, and more.

CASE STUDY

ENOVATION CONTROLS

When you think of innovative organizations that provide a best-of-breed health benefits package and spend far less than peer organizations, you wouldn't necessarily think of small manufacturers in Oklahoma, where as much as 75 percent of the population doesn't have an established primary care relationship. Yet Enovation Controls, a provider of products and services for engine-driven equipment management and control solutions with about 600 employees, has managed to save approximately $4,000 per covered life each year by working with a transparent medical market (TMM).

A TMM puts together a network of the highest-value providers for different kinds of care and gives self-insured employers a set of fair and fully transparent pricing—typically a bundled price—for medical services/procedures ranging from a specific treatment (e.g., knee replacement or coronary stent) to a specific condition (e.g., diabetes or kidney disease) across multiple providers, and sometimes, multiple settings.

Enovation Controls chose The Zero Card to manage their TMM. They achieved a 70 percent participation rate among eligible plan members, focusing on high-cost services like surgeries and imaging. Justin Bray, Enovation's vice president for organizational effectiveness and human resources, attributes the high rate to two primary factors.

1. **Communications** – During the rollout of the TMM, Enovation shared their current health care costs with employees, along with the consequences for the company and each individual. They then compared those costs with the costs of care under specific scenarios with TMM. The message: We've found a better way. Most people were shocked by the vast price disparity and that lower-priced providers often delivered the highest quality, in part because these doctors perform a given procedure more frequentlly, improving with repetition and letting them operate efficiently with fewer errors and expensive complications.

2. **Ease of Use** – Employees have access to a single app or phone number that directs them to network providers where they can get care with zero out-of-pocket costs. Instead of dealing with a mountain of bills and paperwork following the procedure, they receive a thank you survey to ensure the experience went well. As Bray explained, this is particularly critical as surgeries and imaging are some of the highest-cost items they have to cover.

Because of the focus on higher-cost items, Enovation has achieved well over 90 percent of projected savings, even with less than 100 percent participation. The calculation of those potential savings compared the historic "allowable" amount from the company's claims history with a true market amount through the TMM network, that is, what a provider would accept if you showed up with a bag of cash for a bundled procedure such as a total knee replacement.

The savings over historical allowable amounts from their traditional PPO network ranged from 21.92 percent to 81.28 percent, with an average of 59.23 percent.

Here's an example of a line item for one procedure for one employee.

"Spinal fusion except cervical without major complications"

Historic allowed amount	$129,138
TMM network	$38,000
Savings	$91,138

Bray shared what this meant to one employee who came up to him at a high school football game to say thank you. This person had recently had expensive surgery and didn't have to pay a dime out of pocket—no bills, no explanations of benefits, no anything. On a $30,000 salary, the maximum allowable out-of-pocket cost of $2,500 under the previous health plan would have been a financial disaster, the employee said.

Enovation Controls Employee Monthly Premium Costs

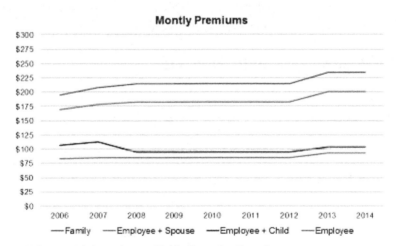

Figure 10. Summary information provided by Enovation Controls.

Like every other health care purchaser, Enovation Controls knows that tackling high-cost procedures is central to slaying the health care cost beast. Its TMM program even extends to items like complex cardiac and neurosurgical procedures, for which employees have access to the same centers of excellence facilities as large employers, such as Cleveland Clinic. Whether the Cleveland Clinic or a local surgery center, high-quality providers are happy to provide a deep discount in return for more business, less hassle, and avoiding claims processing and collections processes. Once the procedure is complete, the provider gets paid within five days for the full bundled price.

Plus, the bundled prices frequently carry warranties, meaning post-surgical complications within 60 to 90 days are addressed at no charge—another bonus for employers.

Using data from Mercer, Enovation Controls estimates that they save $2 million on health care every year, compared with peer manufacturing organizations. For a relatively small company, this is a highly meaningful amount of money, which it has been able to reallocate to increased R&D. While companies in their sector typically spend 4 percent of annual revenues on R&D, Enovation spends 9 percent, helping it stay ahead of the competition and attract and retain the best engineers.

Enovation Controls per capita spending

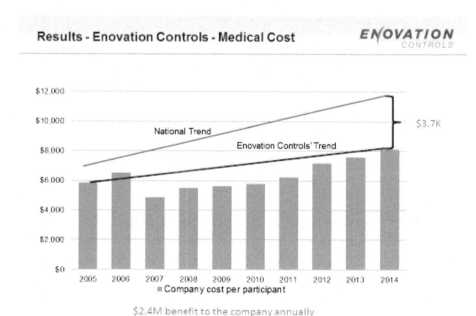

Figure 11. Summary information provided by Enovation Controls.

When a small manufacturer with few dedicated resources can pull this off, it begs the question why every employer or union isn't doing the same. Smart employers like Enovation Controls demonstrate that it's possible even in a state with some of the highest obesity rates and overall health care costs. Since a new primary care model or TMM can be implemented at any point in a benefits cycle, there's no need to wait until renewal.

CHAPTER 16

CONCIERGE-STYLE EMPLOYEE CUSTOMER SERVICE

What Is Concierge-Style Employee Customer Service?

Concierge customer service addresses a substantial challenge that exists for health consumers today—namely that the benefit and health care ecosystems are enormously complex and costly to understand and navigate. Current trends toward high deductible plan design only amplify the time and money required by you and your employees to make more intelligent decisions. Proliferation of solutions that address one or two discrete consumer needs, such as scheduling, price transparency, or finding a provider, still leave the individual to synthesize information across disparate sources, often during a serious health crisis.

Concierge service is the conductor that harmonizes much of this discord and fragmentation, providing one point of interaction and distilling complex information down to actionable guidance.

How Does It Work?

Concierge services are available as a subscription benefit for employees in value-based reimbursement contexts. They come in different forms. At one extreme, there are progressive concierge services driven entirely by algorithms that offer guidance based on machine learning. At the other extreme, there are more traditional, high-touch one-on-one concierge services. In the middle, there are hybrid models built on "human-driven" technology, offering a balance between live support and technology-driven solutions. Members can speak with live support or, if they prefer, navigate through an intuitive mobile or web interface.

Members can access a broad spectrum of support services in a single interaction or series of interactions. Specifically, the concierge can provide:

- Triage
- Explanations of appropriate and available care
- Selection of plan-approved locations
- Help scheduling care
- Cost estimates
- Advocacy for claims and billing questions

The key to an effective concierge experience is integration of information so employees have hassle-free access to simple and actionable guidance on any issue when they need it. To make this work, concierge services are ingesting more and more data to improve the value of their support, tapping into information about plan design, provider networks, real-time benefit consumption (e.g., deductible and out-of-pocket status), individual preferences, and care costs and quality data.

Why Should You Support It?

Concierge services integrate and coordinate a vast array of fragmented solutions into one location, enhancing engagement and optimizing benefit use to lower costs.

Employees who understand the implications of their consumption decisions are empowered to more intelligently navigate the care system. This means they can avoid unnecessary expense. As consumers use concierge services frequently and stretch their health care dollars further, risk bearing employers, insurers, and providers can accrue savings as well.

Many programs that employers have invested significant dollars in, like value-based primary care or the small number of proper workplace wellness programs, require years to deliver return on investment. Concierge services can deliver savings in year one by guiding your employees away from unnecessary, high-cost care.

Concierge support at "critical moments" builds lasting affinity among employees. Helping individuals understand their benefits and access the optimal care in a time of need capitalizes on powerful teachable moments to build awareness of how individuals can be smarter health care consumers on an everyday basis.

Finally, concierge services can be implemented off cycle and introduced successfully in advance of open enrollment as a benefit that can help employees select the best plan for their circumstance. Many times, employees are more comfortable selecting higher deductible plans when they know they will have concierge support as they navigate the care system.

What are The Key Elements to Look for?

1. Network Directories

Robust concierge offerings integrate the appropriate provider directories to accommodate complex network designs, including centers of excellence, onsite care clinics, or narrow networks. The concierge directs members to the highest tier in-network providers for the highest-level of care at the lowest cost, avoiding network leakage and the costs incurred as a result.

2. Price Transparency

Concierge services should help employees prepare both clinically and financially for appointments by explaining the cost of an encounter upfront.

3. Scheduling Capability

Exceptional concierge services go a step beyond and schedule care on the employee's behalf.

4. Understanding of the Individual Consumer

A hallmark of true concierge care is a deep understanding of the individual consumer—including preferences and health profiles—so that care itineraries are personalized and thus more likely to be followed.

How Can You Ensure Quality?

Before contracting with a concierge service—and when considering renewal—ask to see documentation of the following.

- **Engagement** – What portion of a concierge service's addressable population is using the service and how frequently?
- **User satisfaction** – What is the Net Promoter Score associated with the concierge service? Would members recommend it to a friend or loved one?
- **Savings** – What savings has the concierge service delivered for members to date?
- **Marketing support** – What steps does the service take to reinforce member awareness on a regular basis through marketing campaigns, webinars, incentives, etc.?

What Challenges Can You Expect?

1. Employee Education

Such models will require continuing messaging and clear, easy to understand action steps so that concierge services remain top-of-mind for employees when the need arises.

2. Data Sharing

It could be difficult for your concierge service to obtain pricing and quality information from local providers. Since it is your spend, you have a right to this information and experienced concierges can overcome this barrier.

What Action Steps Can You Take?

Ask your broker, consultant, insurer, or TPA if they are familiar with concierge offerings and how they may benefit your health plan.

Evaluate the return on investment from your current benefits toolbox by assessing member utilization rates and savings. If employees aren't using the tools, they may be overly complex, incomplete, or fragmented.

Survey your employees' aptitude for understanding and efficiently navigating the benefits landscape. Do they have an easily accessible resource to guide them through the lifecycle of a health care episode? Are they able to use the appropriate resources at the appropriate time to make educated decisions at the point of service?

Additional Resources

Please go to healthrosetta.org/health-rosetta for ongoing updates, including lists of concierge customer service organizations, case studies, best practices, toolkits, and more.

CHAPTER 17

HIGH-VALUE, TRANSPARENT TPA

What is a High-Value, Transparent TPA?

Third-party administrators (TPAs) charge a monthly fee for paying claims and performing other administrative functions for self-insured employers' health plans. Administrative services organizations (ASOs) associated with large carriers perform similar functions.* However, a high-value, transparent TPA does more. It can transform health care benefits from a black-box line item that increases by double digits each year to a cost-center that you can actively manage and control. The value is evident in dramatic cost reductions that can be as high as 40-50 percent.

As a result, more and more employers are looking beyond large, well-known insurance carriers and have instead embraced local, regional, or national TPAs to help them translate health care costs into known, actionable components.

How Does It Work?

Employers can choose whether to bundle the services they want in their monthly fee, depending on how engaged they want

---

ASOs often refer to themselves as TPAs. For clarity, when I refer to TPAs, I'm referring to TPAs independent of large insurance companies. See Chapter 13 for a more complete explanation of the distinction between ASO and independent TPA.

to be. Most high-value TPAs offer employers a range of provider networks (or no network at all, if you prefer) and integrate other innovative, third-party solutions to tackle costs and/or improve member experience.

A high-value TPA researches the cost of health care services and recommends actions that employers can take to save money. The following chart, adapted from the Colorado Business Group on Health, illustrates how astute employers and their high-value TPA partners measure and act on their employee's health care data.

Care Type	Measure	Action
Chronic care	Incidence/rate of chronic illness, gaps in care, and variation in physician practice patterns	Increase access to and payment for high-value primary care; educate about, remind, and encourage patient adherence
Episodic/outpatient services	Unwarranted variation in pricing for generally undifferentiated services; overutilization of procedures driven by specialists and inappropriate demand	Increase employee education and decision support; pay for and encourage second opinions
Tertiary care	Variation in cost/outcomes by hospital service line	Designate centers of excellence; expose quality data by hospital and service line

Why Should You Support It?

Employers using high-value, transparent TPAs can actively reduce unnecessary health care costs while boosting the quality of health care services, thus improving the health and experience of employees and their families. If you are self-insured and purchasing care using, in part, your employees' money, this should be the minimum fulfillment of your fiduciary responsibilities.

Good health not only improves morale and productivity, it enables you to spend less on health care and more on growing your business. And employers have a unique ability to lead the change in health care that is so critical for the economy.

Sticking with a big-name insurance carrier through an ASO may feel like an easy, safe way to provide health benefits to your employees, which it certainly can be. However, employers who choose to partner with a high-value, transparent TPA typically do so because they are sick of convoluted rules, data that aren't actionable, opaque provider contracts, constant administrative runaround, and paying unknown and irrational amounts in exchange for services that don't add value.

A high-value TPA enables high-value primary care, concierge customer service, transparent medical networks, centers of excellence, and more. In sum, it enables control over health care costs.

It's the first step towards fixing health care in America.

What Are the Key Elements to Look for?

1. Health Care Cost Transparency

Cost transparency means that the TPA helps you see how much you should be paying (the fair market price) for distinct services and price variance between providers. This can be achieved by standardizing prices according to regional benchmarks or Medicare pricing.

2. Quality Data

Having access to reliable data on hospital and/or physician performance is a necessary starting point for developing centers of excellence and other approaches to managing high-cost procedures. While quality data are still imperfect in health care, they are a necessary and valuable starting point for directing care. A high-value TPA will be adept at navigating the various sources of data.

3. Utilization Data

Health care utilization numbers without relevant bench-marks are useless. A high-value TPA will focus on appropriate use of services at the right time, right price, and right location or care setting. It does this by tackling underuse of primary and secondary preventive services for people with chronic conditions and overuse of low-value episodic treatments that are often not medically necessary.

For example, the following list of low-value services was developed by the Oregon Health Council. A high-value TPA can help reduce these wasteful services.

- Outpatient upper endoscopy
- Outpatient MRI, CT, and PET screening
- Spine surgery for pain
- Orthopedic joint procedures
- PTCA
- Stents
- CABG surgery
- Nuclear cardiology diagnostics
- Electron beam computerized tomography (EBCT/SPECT)
- Hysterectomy

4. Continuous Progress

Every region and employer has similar but different chal-lenges. Progress requires continued diligence and improvement over time. High-value TPAs recommend and implement solu-tions to further this goal—the work is never done.

5. Positive Financial Outcomes

Depending on the size and location of the employer, employee demographics, strategies implemented, and regional health care dynamics, financial outcomes may be immediate or unfold over time. For example, an employer investing in direct primary care may see increased costs in the first year as employees begin to work through delayed health issues and adopt healthier behaviors. Often these costs are recouped several times over in years two and three. It is also important to understand which costs can be influenced and which cannot. A high-value, transparent TPA may deliver tangible savings in utilization or unit costs even if you have an overall increase in health care expenditures due to a greater than expected number of high-cost events.

6. Engaged, Satisfied Employees

Saving money in health care requires employees to be educated, engaged participants in their health. Not all employees welcome this responsibility. However, the best TPAs build trust and empower individuals through education and reinforcement of good choices. Overall, they help save money and please employees at the same time.

How Can You Ensure Quality?

It may feel like you're venturing into foreign territory. You're not the first to act to get your employees and you a better deal, so reach out to those who have already benefited from using a high-value TPA, starting with other employers in your area. Here are some resources to help you navigate the path.

Business Groups on Health are nonprofit organizations that support employers in purchasing and managing health care benefits. **Catalyst for Payment Reform** is an independent, national non-profit organization for employers committed to a higher-value health care system that can help navigate complex changes in value-based payment models.

What Challenges Can You Expect?

1. Administrative Challenges

Your broker, consultant, or benefits manager may be unable or unwilling to facilitate a true evaluation of TPA attributes (retention bonuses from ASOs being the primary reason).

2. Employee Education

A high-value, transparent TPA can sometimes feel like more of a change than employees are willing to undertake. Education about why you are tackling health care costs directly is critical to fostering more engaged employees.

3. Fear of Change

There is extraordinary inertia in health care. Most company benefits departments prefer not to rock the boat and stay with known vendors, even when they don't perform.

4. Advisor Conflicts of Interest

Many brokers have undisclosed financial arrangements that favor the status quo and/or incentivize higher health care costs.

What Action Steps Can You Take?

Ask your broker, consultant, or local business group on health if they are currently working with or have experience with a high-value, transparent TPA.

Encourage your broker, consultant, or benefits manager to arrange presentations from TPAs operating in your market.

Revamp your RFPs and annual service provider evaluations to incorporate attributes of high-value, transparent TPAs. Ask your high-value, primary care provider which TPAs they like to work with.

Review all responses to your RFP, not just the ones with the lowest quotes. Sometimes value is not apparent from just looking at the bottom line numbers.

Additional Resources

Please go to healthrosetta.org/health-rosetta for ongoing updates, including lists of high-value, transparent TPA organizations, case studies, best practices, toolkits, and more.

CHAPTER 18

TRANSPARENT PHARMACY BENEFITS

Transparent Pharmacy Benefits should offer purchasers the ability to gain control of decision making based on factual, fully disclosed information. Before we get started though, it's worth noting that the term transparency is incredibly over-used in the market and not all transparency is created equal. It's critical to look behind any seemingly impressive pricing or numbers to get to the real underlying issues that drive costs. I only use the term here for lack of a better one.

Let's start with the key elements and goals of Transparent Pharmacy Benefits.

1. It enables better decisions regarding pharmacy benefits by obtaining and using the data that a purchaser rightly owns.
2. It provides identifiable and measurable metrics to assert pricing and operational control over Pharmacy Benefit Manager (PBM) services.
3. It ensures members have relevant information to make informed choices.
4. It ensures clinical decisions are based solely on efficacy and actual cost, thereby advancing the purchaser's best interests ahead of a vendor's best interests.

Why Should You Support It?

Supporting Transparent Pharmacy Benefits is positive for almost all parties involved. Reducing therapy cost encourages pharmacy benefit participants to become more engaged in their therapy. And there are literally thousands of opportunities where, with proper information and education, participants can make better financial choices and even improve the chances of a quality outcome.

Tim Thomas, CEO of Crystal Clear Rx, gave the following example. Metformin, a drug for treating diabetes, has been around for decades and is a valuable therapy for treating the condition. It is a twice a day drug and can be obtained for less than $40 a month. Today, there are new formulations of Metformin that can be taken once a day, possibly improving patient adherence, but at a much greater cost to the participant and employer, over $3,000 a month. If the participant was educated and properly incentivized, would they be able to maintain adherence and reduce spending by nearly $36,000 per year? Pharmacists that have additional training and are paid appropriately for their time can help patients with this situation as well.

How Does It Work?

Compared to some Health Rosetta components, Transparent Pharmacy Benefits don't actually work much differently than what you're used to. The primary difference is the process for engaging your consultant or PBM services vendor. It focuses on contracts, access to data, and distribution channels for accessing drugs that counteract the pricing opacity, undisclosed financial incentives, and other conflicts that permeate status quo pharmacy benefits. The most critical piece is the role and involvement of an expert who knows the space top to bottom and has incentives aligned with your interests.

What Are the Key Elements to Look For?

1. Clarity on How PBMs Work

PBM business models and revenue streams are often highly-complex and full of conflicts that make their incentives very different than yours or your plan members. To start, they are often incentivized to push certain prescription brands. Additionally, "rebates" can be misleading and may not result in actual savings. True transparency is needed. Rebates can be up to 25% of the total cost of a brand or specialty drug and rarely benefit the member as they are paid to the plan sponsor or health plan. Thus, PBMs use rebate incentives that benefit only the plan sponsor or health plan at the expense of the patient through increased drug costs at the point of sale. Plus, the definition of what is a rebate payable to the plan sponsor or health plan rarely aligns with the actual amount paid by pharmaceutical manufacturers to the PBM. True transparency means one can see the relevant contracts the PBM has with manufacturers and others.

Some PBMs also employ pricing tactics that create "spread pricing" in which the amount charged to you and your members or a health plan is drastically higher than what is actually paid to the pharmacy. Spread pricing occurs across brand, specialty, and generic drugs. It's especially egregious in the generic component.

2. Access to Your Claims Data

Pharmacy claims data is some of the most robust and readily available in the health care industry, but first you need to get access to it, then fully understand and utilize it.

Next, your PBM relationship and agreements should make clear that you own your claims data as the purchaser of services. This includes your right to use that data to make informed decisions. You should combine your data with other analytical resources to analyze the true cost of pharmacy treatments and not solely depend on information the PBM provides.

Access to this data is essential to operating an effective ERISA plan. ERISA health plan service providers typically abdicate fiduciary responsibilities in their contracts with your plan. This means not getting data can increase your own risk under ERISA's fiduciary requirements to manage the plan solely for the benefit of the plan members.

3. Complete Contract Understanding

A complete understanding of current PBM contracts, utilizing a neutral third-party consultant, will ensure you have a clear understanding of current terms and conditions that are often the source of hidden costs. Even definitions left in OR OUT of a contract can be financially devastating.

This is especially true when it comes to "guarantees" in the PBM-purchaser contract. Average Wholesale Price (AWP) with its associated "discount" is the common method for evaluating PBM financial performance. AWP really means "Any Wild-assed Price" or "Ain't What's Paid" to be less snarky. Because AWP is often confusing and misleading, it can reduce leverage in negotiations.

Scott Haas, an industry expert, provided Figure 12 on the next page as an example of how AWP can and often does produce pricing variability to the plan sponsor and member. It is data from a real contract with a uniform AWP-68.5% discount for retail generics. First, notice the price per unit varies dramatically even though this is supposedly a uniform discount. Second, the unit costs rise over time. PBMs will say this is your cost trend, but it's often the PBM increasing cost basis to increase their spread (and revenue) over time. As a result, AWP-based discounts and metrics make it far harder to see or manage actual spending.

Another issue is distribution channel pricing variability, such as mail order and specialty.

The foregoing are just a couple examples of how the many moving pieces of PBM contracts, claims processing approaches, and business practices can make it difficult to manage spend. You need the right oversight and contract terms.

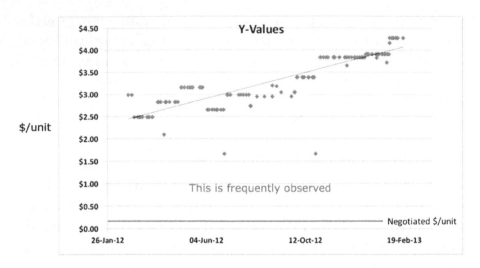

Figure 12: The contracted AWP-68.5% discount remained the same for the entire period. Each point represents a single claim. Source: Scott Haas.

4. Expert Resources

Purchasers should pair their own data with unbiased consultants equipped with analytical know how, pharmacy industry knowledge, and vendor insight to negotiate better PBM contracts. Then they can decide for themselves if they should leave all of the PBM services with one vendor or if they should carve out certain aspects of the pharmacy benefit.

Consultants who only work with PBMs that pay them disclosed or undisclosed fees should be avoided. Having the wrong economic incentives makes it nearly impossible to act in the best interests of their clients. Many PBM coalitions should also be looked at with suspicion because of the lack of overall transparency and potential fiduciary duty issues under ERISA. Follow the money before trusting any arrangement that doesn't let you view the contract between the PBM and Coalition sponsor. Without it, you can't fully assess whether that arrangement will truly provide you the value represented.

5. Creative Distribution Channels

What if mail order prescriptions are actually costing you more than the same drug at retail? Seriously, this happens. When evaluating a PBM's channels, consider carving out mail order and specialty pharmacy services from the PBM contract. Some mail order and specialty pharmacies offer services for "cost plus a management fee," which can be far less expensive than the AWP "Ain't What's Paid" model. Plan design often drives whether this is a cost effective solution.

What Challenges Can You Expect?

1. The Appearance of Savings

Consultants and PBMs will use AWP discounts that *appear* to create significant cost savings. Remember, AWP is a flawed metric for analysis that clouds true costs and any potential savings. A good analogy for this core flaw is what happens when you multiply percentages of percentages. The math quickly gets so convoluted that it just doesn't work well.

During the RFP process, most consultants send your current pharmacy claims data to other PBMs, who then reprice the claims, showing you what you would have paid under their pricing (again, often using AWP). Since every proposal always has the appearance of savings, you'd think just doing an RFP each year would give you negative pharmacy costs eventually. Unfortunately, this isn't the case.

The core problem with this is the flawed process. How much can you trust RFP responses when your consultant just gives your data to a potential vendor without controlling anything that occurs when repricing that data for the response? Because the actual repricing work is done by the PBM vying for your business, the consultant can't have any real confidence it's done correctly.

Plus, very few consultants compare actual pharmacy claims to original RFP responses to ensure the original representations actually materialized in reality after the contract was signed.

A better process is for your consultant to provide very basic summary information to PBM vendors about your plan, employees, total spend, prices paid through various channels, and other plan design elements. Then, they require PBMs to provide brand and specialty pricing, plus fixed per pill unit costs for generics (usually around 3,000 of them) that have some guaranteed pricing or utilize a MAC (Maximum Allowable Cost) list. Lastly, they will apply the responses to your actual data to create a cost avoidance summary that provides accurate and statistically validated cost saving potential (absent specialty utilization).

There's far more complexity to this, but the key point is you need someone that applies the type of statistical discipline that would make an auditor proud. Handing data over to health plans or PBMs without provable validation controls isn't enough.

2. Interference

Many PBMs talk transparency, but it is *not* in their best financial interests. Existing consultants who are being incentivized by payments from PBMs may interfere with your journey toward transparency, as it may not be in their best financial interest.

3. Lack of Understanding

Although this may not be an obvious pain point, there still might be a lack of understanding in the HR department about the benefits of Transparent Pharmacy Benefits, or they may simply be unaware of the options available. It is important to gain HR and executive buy-in.

4. Not All Transparency Is Equal

There is often confusion between transparent and transparent passthrough. Transparent does not necessarily mean you are getting pass through pricing and the pricing being passed through may not be the best available. Make sure you understand the different models and that the transparency is working its way to you and in your favor. Just because a vendor claims to be transparent, this doesn't mean they're the best option, able to secure the best pricing, or even meaningfully transparent.

5. Obfuscation to Preserve Status Quo

Consultants and PBM's who aren't forward-looking may fall back on "fear, uncertainty, and doubt" tactics meant to freeze progress. As stewards of your organization's and employees' hard-earned money, you must choose whether to protect your own health and bottom line or that of your vendor.

What Action Steps Can You Take?

Ask your broker, consultant, advisor, insurance carrier, or TPA if they are currently working with or have experience with transparent pharmacy benefits.

Ask your broker, consultant, or advisorif they or their firm receive any compensation from any PBMs or service provider?

Ask these same parties how they recognize the difference between good and bad pricing?

Encourage your broker, consultant, advisor, insurance carrier, or TPA to find, interpret, and share reliable cost and quality data from pharmacy benefits managers competing for your business.

Consider comparing pharmacy benefits managers through a structured and disciplined RFP process.

Get access to your own data to go beyond AWP and other misleading cost metrics to help you understand the real prices you're paying for each drug in your plan.

Additional Resources

Please visit healthrosetta.org/health-rosetta for ongoing updates, including lists of vendors, case studies, best practices, toolkits, and more.

CHAPTER 19

"ERISA FIDUCIARY RISK IS THE LARGEST UNDISCLOSED RISK I'VE SEEN IN MY CAREER"

Written with Sean Schantzen

The Employee Retirement Income Security Act of 1974 (ERISA) is a federal law that sets minimum standards for most voluntarily established pension and health plans in private industry to protect the individuals in these plans. Plan trustees (typically company boards, plan administrators, and others) have fiduciary duties to ERISA plans to ensure these protections are implemented and managed in a plan.

Most people know the law in relation to retirement benefits, but it is emerging as an unexpected, yet high-potential, opportunity to drive change in the dysfunctional U.S. health care system. This is because roughly 100 million Americans receive health benefits through self-insured ERISA plans, accounting for more than $1 trillion in annual healthcare spending (including out-of-pocket spending by plan members). Companies spend roughly double on ERISA health plans what they spend on ERISA retirement plans.

Increased outside scrutiny of how ERISA-regulated health plans spend their dollars is creating immense potential liability for companies, officers, directors, and even health insurers across the country. The quote that is this chapter's title came from a prominent risk management practice leader with one of the Big Four accounting firms at an event I attended on payment integrity (i.e., fraud prevention). We are also starting to see this in benefits departments—one entire benefits department at a large, well-known company was fired (with the exception of one person) when their board realized the lack of proper management.

While employer and union health plans are roughly one-half of all healthcare spending, they likely represent over two-thirds of healthcare industry profits because they frequently wildly overpay for health care services, partially as a result of misperceptions like the ones outlined in Chapter 6.

This is also where a large opportunity to reduce legal risk and increase financial performance exists. Health care is the last major bucket of operating expenses that most companies still aren't actively optimizing and managing like similarly large P&L line items. This makes ERISA plans an attractive target for operational efficiencies.

Doing this is simpler than most think. ERISA requires plan trustees to prudently manage health plan assets. Yet very few plans have the functional equivalent of an ERISA retirement plan administrator that actively manages and drives effective allocation of plan investments, either internally or externally. This person or team should have the deep actuarial and health care expertise highlighted at the end of Chapter 9, something traditional human resource departments usually lack.

Employers can also do something about the enormous fraud and waste in the system. As we saw in Chapter 7, most employers are doing little or nothing to prevent fraud because they typically aren't aware of its extent or that it's even happening. *The Economist* has reported that fraudulent health care claims alone consume $272 billion of spending each year across both private plans and public programs like Medicare and Medicaid.[102] The Institute of Medicine's study on waste in the U.S. health care system concluded that $750 billion, or 25% of all spending, is waste.[103] It's impossible to imagine any CEO, CFO, or board allowing this in any other area of their company.

Could Emerging Litigation Be Our Savior?

Key events suggest that increased scrutiny of ERISA fiduciary duties is upon us.

First, two Big Four accounting firms have refused in certain circumstances to sign off on audits that don't make allowances for ERISA fiduciary risk. At a meeting I attended in the last year, a senior risk management practice leader at one of those firms told a room of health care entrepreneurs and experts that ERISA fiduciary risk was the largest undisclosed risk they'd seen in their career. As more accounting firms follow suit, it could require employers to change how they manage ERISA health plans.

Second, independent board directors have quietly sounded the alarm to auditors of three separate companies (that I'm aware of) about the potential for personal financial liability that director and officer insurance policies may not cover. We expect to see more focus on this issue, given that health care spending is roughly 20% of payroll spending for most companies.

Third, regulatory scrutiny is beginning to increase on a number of fronts. Here's just one example. In September 2017, the Department of Labor brought a case against Macy's and two of its third party administrators alleging violations of ERISA's fiduciary rules, largely relating to payment of out-of-network healthcare claims.[104] It also included alleged violations of some newer wellness program rules. This is just one example of various types of attention and scrutiny we're seeing emerge.

Fourth, attorneys are actively cultivating cases and litigation strategies in which employers will file suits against their ERISA plan co-trustees or vendors, primarily the plan administrators who actively manage the plan's health dollars. These center on allegations that the co-trustees or vendors breached ERISA fiduciary duties or other related duties by turning a blind eye to fraudulent claims. We expect the number of these cases to significantly increase in the next couple years. One firm we're aware of is cultivating dozens of these cases.

The implications of this fourth trend could be enormous: If boards and plan trustees know meaningful fraud could exist and don't take action to rectify the issues, they could open themselves to liability from shareholders, plan beneficiaries, and others. The magnitude of damages just for fraudulent claims could be similar to asbestos and tobacco lawsuits. Conservative fraudulent claims estimates are ~5% and many believe 10%-15% is more accurate.[105] Employers spend more than $1 trillion per year through ERISA helath benefits plans. Extrapolating the 5% estimate over ERISA's six-year lookback period for damages from fiduciary duty breaches, this could create $300 billion in potential damages.

These potentially significant legal risks should prompt employers to more actively manage health spending the same way they manage other large operating expenses. As we've learned in this book, companies already doing this are reducing their health benefits spending by 20% or more, while providing superior benefits packages.

They use a variety of approaches, but most are relatively straightforward and focus on proven benefits-design solutions that make poor care decisions more costly and better care decisions less costly. Most importantly, they don't focus on shifting costs to employees, but on tackling pricing failure, fraud, overuse, misdiagnosis, and sub-optimal treatment—the sources of most wasted spending. Finally, there are people that can help companies of all sizes in any geography implement these solutions and build better-managed plans.

Time and again, we've found that the best way to slash costs is to improve health benefits.

Sean Schantzen was previously a securities attorney involved in representing boards, directors, officers, and companies in securities litigation, corporate transaction, and other matters. He is my co-founder in the Health Rosetta ecosystem.

ERISA Sample Plan Document Checklist

The Department of Labor describes the fiduciary duty and potential liability as follows:

Fiduciaries have important responsibilities and are subject to standards of conduct because they act on behalf of participants in a group health plan and their beneficiaries. These responsibilities include:

- *Acting solely in the interest of plan participants and their beneficiaries and with the exclusive purpose of providing benefits to them;*
- *Carrying out their duties prudently;*
- *Following the plan documents (unless inconsistent with ERISA);*
- *Holding plan assets (if the plan has any) in trust; and*
- *Paying only reasonable plan expenses.*

Liability

With these fiduciary responsibilities, there is also potential liability. Fiduciaries who do not follow the basic standards of conduct may be personally liable to restore any losses to the plan, or to restore any profits made through improper use of the plan's assets resulting from their actions.

If an employer contracts with a plan administrator to manage the plan, the employer is responsible for the selection of the service provider, but is not liable for the individual decisions of that provider. However, an employer is required to monitor the service provider periodically to assure that it is handling the plan's administration prudently

To keep from falling short, fiduciaries should address the following items of language in negotiations with vendors and/or providers. (These are general guidelines to use as a starting point; please consult your own ERISA attorney for specific advice and a more comprehensive assessment.)

Allowable Payment Amounts

- "Usual and customary" or similar language is by far the most common way that health plans cut costs. Definitions of this term vary from very weak to very strong. Ideal language allows the plan administrator to pay the lesser of certain amounts based on costs, Medicare allowable amounts, etc., although a negotiated rate should always be paid to avoid breaching a network or direct contract.
- Although any claim can potentially be negotiated with the right tools, this is much more difficult if the plan document does not have language permitting negotiation (and falling back to low "usual and customary rates" in the absence of a negotiation).
- Wrap networks accessed by plans can result in little cost-savings with high fees. For this reason, we recommend an unwrapped service, which helps the plan define a reasonable and fair market, value-based allowable amount for all out-of-network claims – including those that would otherwise be sent to wrap networks – with defensible claims repricing, patient advocacy, and back-end balance-billing support to boot.

Experimental or Investigational

- "Experimental" should explicitly reference criteria such as industry-standards, accepted medical practice, service rendered on a research basis, clinical trials, and peer-reviewed literature.
- Noteworthy facets of this language that are sometimes brought into question include off-label drugs and com-

pound drugs. The plan should clearly state how it will treat such claims.

Medical Necessity

- As long as it defines medical necessity based on objective criteria, this language should be acceptable. Ideal criteria include treatment meant to restore health and otherwise appropriate under the circumstances according to the AMA or other sources. It does not include treatment that is maintenance or custodial in nature or disallowed by Medicare.
- Make sure the language does not leave the determination of medical necessity to the discretion of the treating provider; the plan administrator should always retain this discretion.

Plan Administrator Discretion

- While every plan document necessarily gives the plan administrator discretion to determine payment amounts, watch out for instances where the administrator has too much or not enough discretion. Discretion should be granted to interpret the plan document's provisions and determine issues of fact related to claims for benefits.
- A provision to cover nearly anything the administrator deems appropriate may well cause a stop-loss reimbursement issue.

Fiduciary Duties

- For both self-funding veterans and those new to the industry, managing the fiduciary duties associated with making claims determinations can be a daunting task.
- Outsourcing fiduciary duties for final-level internal

appeals is the most efficient and cost-effective way of handling this responsibility. Leading ERISA firms provide an approach that shifts the fiduciary burden of handling final-level appeals onto a neutral third-party.

Coordination of Benefits

- If the plan is always the primary payer, that presents a cost-containment problem; It should pay secondary in all conceivable situations (with the exception of Medicare or when otherwise not permitted) and clearly say so in the plan document.
- Ideal language will describe which plan pays primary/secondary in certain circumstances.

Leaves of Absence

- Many health plans provide coverage for any period of approved leave as determined by the employer. This can translate into individuals being covered based solely on "internal" leave policies of the employer, which are sometimes not even written, or determined on a case-by-case basis by the employer.
- While this is not a problem for the plan document per se, it is a very common problem when it comes to stop-loss reimbursement for claims incurred while an employee is on such an approved leave of absence.

Employee Skin in the Game

- Some employers elect to offer members certain incentives for performing tasks such as choosing certain providers over others, auditing bills for correctness, and purchasing durable medical equipment online at discounted rates rather than from hospitals.

- Typical rewards include offering the member a percentage of savings achieved by the plan or waiving coinsurance and deductibles.

Exclusions

- The plan document should exclude claims that result from "illegal acts." There are different ways to structure this exclusion that can increase or decrease the potential for exposure.
- Another important exclusion is for claims resulting from "hazardous activities," i.e., activities with a greater-than-normal likelihood of injury.

Overpayment Recovery and Third Party Recovery

- To maximize recoveries, the plan document needs both strong language describing the plan's reimbursement rights and a partnership with a recovery vendor that excels at enforcing the plan's rights.
- Third-party recovery provisions should include:

  - Disclaimer of the "made-whole" and "common fund" doctrines
  - Ability to recover from estates, wrongful death proceeds, and the legal guardians of minors.
  - Ability to offset any funds recovered by the patient but unpaid to the plan

Compliance and General Drafting

- The terms of the plan document must be compliant with applicable law, including ERISA, HIPAA, COBRA, and many others, in addition to any applicable state law.
- Some in the industry feel that the plan document and

summary plan description must be separate documents, but leading ERISA attorneys say that one single document suffices for both.

- The terms of the plan document must be consistent and clear; without being ambiguous, they should still allow for some interpretation by the plan administrator.

Please visit healthrosetta.org/health-rosetta for ongoing updates, including lists of vendors, case studies, best practices, toolkits, and more.

CHAPTER 20

THE OPIOID CRISIS: EMPLOYERS HAVE THE ANTIDOTE

Tom L. Shupe is a senior manager at an Oklahoma manufacturer. For 37 years, he has been on the frontlines of the challenges facing U.S. manufacturing. He's full of insight, but the most surprising is that he blames substance abuse—specifically opioids—for the majority of these challenges. "It's all addiction issues," says Shupe. He calls the opioid crisis, which is really an epidemic of addiction, "probably the biggest threat in manufacturing, period." [106]

Here's something even more shocking: Employers are unwitting accomplices, enablers, and victims of this public health crisis, the largest since the 1918 flu epidemic.

Let's look at just one example. A major challenge of physically demanding, hourly jobs is that if you don't work, you don't get paid. An injured worker must choose between not working and not getting paid, or continuing to work in pain and getting paid. Opioids start as a short-term fix, enabling the worker to stay on the job, but they also slow healing—and can even prevent it. If the worker has the predisposition to addiction, this launches a vicious escalating cycle.

There is a growing trend that equates long-term chronic pain patients with people suffering from opioid addictions. There are an array of rare diseases, such as Ehlers–Danlos syndrome, where well-managed opioid regimens can be the appropriate course of treatment. We must be careful that the zeal to address the opioid crisis doesn't inflict unnecessary suffering on those with these types of long-term chronic pain. This is where physicians having adequate time to treat patients as individuals is imperative. Other countries manage to work with these long-term pain patients without the opioid crisis that America is dealing with.

Beyond the obvious human toll, there is a compelling business imperative to solve this crisis. Supporting early identification of addiction, along with access to effective treatment and relapse prevention, doesn't just help the sick and suffering. It makes great *economic* sense in ways we'll discuss throughout this chapter.

Make no mistake: The opioid crisis is a complicated issue over thirty years in the making. But companies have played a major role in creating and sustaining the crisis. However, a vanguard of employers are realizing that they have a major role to play in solving it, recognizing the solutions fall well beyond what the government alone can do. The opioid epidemic is a microcosm and mirror of the role employers can play in creating and fixing our failing health system as a whole. Ending it will meaningfully move us down the path to solving our larger health crisis.

Primary Drivers

There are 12 primary drivers of the opioid crisis, all of which must be addressed by the country and, specifically, by employers.

1. Economic distress

Drug, alcohol, and suicide mortality rates are higher in counties with more economic distress and a larger working class. Many counties with these high mortality rates have also seen significant manufacturing employment losses over the past several decades.[107] For every 1% rise in unemployment, there's a 4% rise in addiction and a 7% increase in emergency department visits.[108] Remember health care costs can consume as much as 50% of an employee's total compensation package for the half of the workforce making less than $15 per hour.[109] For many, many industries, health care costs are the primary driver suppressing wages and job growth.

2. Health-related state/local budget challenges weaken community resilience

Governments can only raise taxes so much. We've seen how out-of-control health care costs have eaten away at the very items that make a community more resistant to public health challenges. Nearly every budget item that has been cut or affected is an element of solving the opioid crisis. One example is mental health funding, a particularly powerful antidote to the opioid crisis. At the local level, funding shortfalls are exacerbated by tax-exempt health systems that are often among the largest property owners, yet pay no taxes. Yet America's perverse health care incentives continue to reinforce the common view that building hospitals is an economic driver.

3. Declining physician reimbursement increases likelihood of prescribing

The current reimbursement amounts for most physicians in private practice continues to decline, despite an escalation of both operating costs and administrative burden. As a result, patient volume increases and the average amount of time a provider can spend with each patient decreases. As patient interaction time decreases, the probability of writing an opioid prescription increases.

These pressures to increase volume make it incredibly challenging for most providers, who typically are not well versed in addiction medicine, to identify and effectively manage patients with chronic pain, mental illness, and potentially undiagnosed substance abuse.

4. Mental illness treated with opioids

According to a recent study, more than half of all opioid prescriptions in the United States each year go to adults with a mental illness, yet just 16% of the U.S. population suffers from mental illness.[110] It's important to note that depression and anxiety worsen pain and vice versa. Healthy and effective stress and life-coping skills can decrease the impact of this pain. Converssely, a lack of effective coping skills can leave one vulnerable to experiencing a much greater degree of suffering from pain.

5. Undertreated pain leading to a 5th vital sign

Pain as a vital sign was initially promoted by the American Pain Society to elevate awareness of pain treatment among health care professionals. The Veteran's Health Administration made it a 5th vital sign in 1998, followed by their creation of the "Pain as the 5th Vital Sign Toolkit" in 2000. This made pain equal to things like blood pressure—a number to be managed with medications or lifestyle changes. In 2001, the Joint Commission established standards for pain assessment and treatment in response to the national outcry about widespread undertreatment, putting severe pressure on doctors and nurses to prescribe opioids.

6. Patient satisfaction scores influence hospital income

Results from Press Ganey and HCAHPS patient satisfaction surveys directly impact hospital income, further amping up the pressure. Administrators have often harangued nurses and doctors to make patients happy by giving them opioids.

7. Pharma's sales and marketing blitz

Pharmaceutical companies capitalized on the previous drivers. Through major marketing campaigns,[111] they got physicians to prescribe opioids such as Percocet and OxyContin in high quantities—even though evidence[112] for using opioids to treat long-term, chronic pain is very weak[113] and evidence that they cause long-term harm is very strong.[114] Additionally, no organization has potentially had more ability to flag the growing crisis than pharmacy benefits managers. Instead, they let the crisis explode in severity. In contrast to other countries, U.S. physicians stopped prescribing slow and low, a byproduct of which is that huge amounts of opioids are readily available in medicine cabinets for people suffering any level of pain—and for teenagers to abuse. Direct-to-consumer advertising also significantly increased patient requests for opioid prescriptions.[115]

8. Patients looking for a quick fix

An unfortunate part of American culture is seeking quick fixes. Patients want a pill for instant pain relief and advertising has conditioned them to expect this. This tendency is exacerbated by doctors looking for a quick fix during short appointments with patients. The reality is most patients hear more from pharmaceutical companies (16-18 hours of pharma ads per year[116]) than from their doctor (typically under 2 hours per year).

With this "instant-fix" conditioning from players across the health care system, many patients aren't willing to invest time in things like cognitive behavioral therapy, mindful meditation, or a regular program of physical therapy/exercise. At the same time, we've forgotten that some pain is a good indicator of an issue to solve and shouldn't be instantly numbed.

Ironically, careful opioid-based treatment can be appropriate for some people suffering from certain types of long-term chronic pain, but they are often denied appropriate medications, instructions, or supervision as a result of the other drivers.

9. Opioids used for non-cancer chronic pain (e.g., back pain)

Eighty percent of people will have lower back pain in their lifetime, making it one of the most common reasons for missing work.[117] Stress or inappropriate posture, a sedentary lifestyle, and poor workplace ergonomics can all lead to back, neck, and other kinds of musculoskeletal (MSK) pain. The American Academy of Neurology (AAN) told its members that the risks of opioids in treating noncancer chronic pain patients far outweighed the benefits, yet the practice is widespread. The AAN observed that if physicians stopped using opioids to treat conditions such as fibromyalgia, back pain, and headache, long-term exposure to opioids could decline by as much as 50%.

10. Lack of access to specialists

For many physicians in rural areas, where pain specialists with high-quality experience and training are shockingly rare. The only tool in the toolbox has often been more pills.

11. Criminals abuse of the system

In many locales, doctors lacking ethics have been easier to find than proper pain treatment. "Pill mills" disguised as "pain clinics" gave legitimate pain doctors a bad name. Pharmacy benefits managers and pharmacies were more than willing to go along with the game, making billions in the process. The public and private sector purchasers dropped the ball on this by not having opioid prescribing databases in place to catch the bad actors. As prescription opioid availability has tightened up, cheap black tar heroin has filled the need for individuals suffering from addiction. People addicted to opioids are 40 times more likely to become addicted to heroin.[118]

12. Insurers' refusal to cover validated treatments

Insurance companies have generally refused to cover scientifically validated approaches for pain management—such as mindful meditation, cognitive behavior therapy, psychological support, or interventional pain procedures. Even when a physician appeals to an insurance company to approve treatments that may help the patient, several months or even years can go by, especially in worker's compensation cases.[119] As a result of increased tolerance, the patient may then be on escalating doses of opioids just to function. This results in more anxiety and depression, often leading to financial devastation as a result of losing their employment.

While we are talking about physicians, let's clear up one misunderstanding. Most good doctors, even those who aren't salaried employees, have no financial incentive to get their patients hooked. The waiting lists to be seen by a pain specialist are weeks long and these doctors aren't going to run out of patients anytime soon. The vast majority really want their patients to get better. A chronic pain patient who no longer needs pills or experiences pain is the best marketing a doctor could ask for. Most doctors have been trying to do the right thing based on what they knew about opioids and what insurers would cover.

A Weight Around Employers' Necks

Before delving into the antidotes, let's take a quick look at the damage opioids are wreaking on the American economy in general and employers in particular. This isn't to ignore the immense human suffering caused by the crisis, just to surface other damage that's often not seen or understood.

Here's a good starting point: Opioid related overdoses—often taken in conjunction with other central nervous system depressant drugs like benzodiazepines or alcohol—are now the leading cause of death for working age people under 50 years old, surpassing deaths from guns and car crash.[120]

LinkedIn's Work in Progress podcast had a couple big takeaways on how the opioid crisis negatively impacts employers.[121]

• At a Congressional hearing focused on opioids and their economic consequences, Ohio attorney general Mike DeWine estimated that 40% of job applicants in Ohio either failed or refused a drug test.[122] This results in higher unemployment rates and solid middle class jobs go unfilled. In earlier Congressional testimony from July 2017, Federal Reserve chair Janet Yellen connected opioid use to a decline in the labor participation rate.

- The issue is amplifying labor shortages in industries like trucking, which has had difficulty recruiting qualified workers for the last six years. It's also pushing employers to broaden their job searches, recruiting people from greater distances when positions can't be filled locally. At stake is not just unemployment rates, workplace safety, and productivity—but whether workplaces need humans at all. Some manufacturers claim opioids are forcing them to automate faster.

Some may find drug testing intrusive, but accidents at many jobs—such as manufacturing and transportation—pose potentially huge consequences. For example, opioids were to blame for the Staten Island Ferry disaster that killed 11 and injured dozens.[123] Plus, "presenteeism," where an employee performs sub-optimally while at work, is a very big problem for employers. Impairing pain or medications, especially opioids, often causes this. Unlike cocaine or heroin, where a confirmatory drug screen results in termination, a "legitimate" prescription for Oxycodone and Xanax is a much murkier human resources problem.

The New York Times reported that workers who receive higher doses of opioids to treat injuries like back strain stay out-of-work three times longer than those with similar injuries who receive lower doses.[124] Between disability and medical care payments, the cost of a workplace injury is as much as nine times higher when opioids are used. An employee's medical expenses and lost wage payments averages about $13,000, but this triples to $39,000 when they are prescribed a short-acting painkiller like Percocet—and it triples again to $117,000 when a stronger, longer-acting opioid like OxyContin is prescribed.

In the same article, Dr. Bernyce M. Peplowski, the medical director of the State Compensation Insurance Fund of California said that insurer policies for covering painkillers, but not evidence-based physical therapy approaches, may "have created a monster."

The Path Forward

While we must be smarter about treating those already afflicted with opioid addictions, we must also turn off the spigot to clean up the mess. If there's a silver lining to the opioid crisis at all, it's that it shines a light on just how abysmally our health care system has been performing.

At the end of Sam Quinones' gripping book on the opioid crisis, *Dreamland,* he argues that the sustainable fix is community.

A community that addresses social determinants of health like safe neighborhoods, quality jobs, and a health care system that can treat those afflicted with opioid overuse disorders while preventing others from being drawn into the hell of addiction.

Employers who use the opioid crisis as a catalyst to change their approach to health care also do their broader community a great service. By extension, they help create a better pool of prospective employees to draw on.

When one realizes that the opioid crisis isn't an outlier situation, but a microcosm of our larger health care dysfunction, it's clear how solving one of the largest public health crises in American history is a catalyst for dramatically improving our health care system.

Put simply, employers who adopt Health Rosetta type benefits programs are far more likely to have much lower rates of employees and dependents suffering from opioid overuse disorders.

Let's revisit our 12 drivers with examples of Health Rosetta type benefits from elsewhere in the book to show how this is possible. More details are available at healthrosetta.org.

Opioid crisis driver	Proven employer antidotes
Economic distress	The case study about Tulsa-based Enovation Controls shows how a manufacturer with a blue-collar workforce designed benefits that make smart decisions free (e.g., eliminating copays and deductibles when using high value surgical hospitals) and bad decisions expensive (e.g., going to low quality providers who have higher complication rates, poor outcomes, and overtreatment). (*Case Study: Enovation Controls*)
Health-related state/local budget challenges weaken community resilience	Examples abound in our case studies. On the East coast, the Allegheny County Schools case study shows how steering school district employees and dependents away from low-value (even if high reputation) medical centers can improve teacher pay and reduce class sizes. In the Midwest, the City of Milwaukee has avoided many budget struggles afflicting other large Midwestern cities by controlling health care costs. On the West coast, the city of Kirkland, WA has found that the best way to slash health care costs is to *improve* benefits.[125] While many communities are pulling back on investments that drive health outcomes (walkability, safety, parks, clean air/water), Kirkland is able to maintain or increase these investments in community well-being. (*Case Studies: Pittsburgh Schools; City of Milwaukee*)

Declining physician reimbursement increases likelihood of prescribing	In a value-based primary care model, patients have the proper amount of time with their doctor. More patient interaction time shuts down some of the onramps to opioids, whether it's inappropriate opioid prescribing or unnecessary and excessive surgeries that are typically followed by opioid prescriptions. *(Chapter 13)*
Mental disorders treated with opioids	Evidence-based benefits plans ensure behavioral health is woven into primary care, not an afterthought. A subtle, but critical, success factor is removing barriers to mental health professionals. Where there is sufficient employee concentration, behavioral health services should exist inside clinics, so there's no separate (and potentially stigmatized) visit with a mental health specialist. In other settings, it's more practical to have the mental health specialist connected remotely, an approach that also overcomes the disparity in different locations' access to mental health professionals.

Behavioral health issues are particularly short-changed in the rushed, "drive by" primary care appointments that are all too common in volume-driven primary care. Since mental health issues underlie so many exacerbations of chronic diseases, it is part of the "magic" of proper primary care that there is time to pick up on issues that may keep someone from adhering to a care plan. *(Chapter 13)* |

Undertreated pain leading to a 5th vital sign	Value-based primary care is critical to physicians understanding the issues behind a patient's pain. With MSK-related costs accounting for ~20% of employer health care spending, wise employers integrate physical therapy specialists into primary care and workplace design, leveraging organizations using evidence-based physical therapy upfront in triage of pain. *(Case Study: City of Milwaukee)*
	Appropriate use of drug testing and regular checks of the state prescription drug monitoring reports can help identify a substance abuse disorder earlier, starting the process to wellness. *(Case Study: Rosen Hotel & Resorts)*
Patient satisfaction scores' influence on hospital income	Evidence is mixed on whether patient satisfaction correlates with improved outcomes—or greater inpatient use, higher overall health care & prescription drug spending, and increased mortality.[126] Wise employers contract with health care organizations focused on other metrics. For example, Net Promoter Score (NPS), a measure of customer likelihood to recommend a product or service, is more likely aligned with approaches focused on keeping people well. *(Chapter 1; Chapter 5).*
Big pharmas' sales and marketing blitz	Let's face it, sales and marketing works. If a physician hears more about pharmaceutical approaches than non-pharmaceutical ones, this will influence their behavior. Value-based primary care organizations ensure clinicians receive education on treatment options that maximize value and come from unbiased sources—and have time to explain to patients how non-opioid treatment options are more effective. They also have viable, quantifiable treatment alternatives in place. *(Chapter 11; Chapter 13; Case Study: Langdale Industries)*

Patients looking for a quick fix	Value-based primary care organizations recognize that pain rarely has quick fixes. There is usually some issue beneath the pain and doctors need sufficient time with patients to uncover it.
Opioids used for non-cancer chronic pain (e.g., back pain)	Modern benefits programs weave non-opioid options into both the clinic and non-clinic settings. One example is physical therapy for back pain. Another is Rosen Hotel's incorporating movement training and ergonomic adjustments into the workplace. A well-informed plan should require that certain steps be taken before and after administration of opioids, such as placing a time limit on how long an employee can be authorized to take the medication. *(Chapter 5; Chapter 9; Chapter 10; Chapter 12; Case Study: Rosen Hotel & Resorts)*
Lack of access to specialists	As we have seen, sending employees to centers of excellence and using telemedicine are two increasingly common ways savvy companies are overcoming this problem. From both a lack of specialist access and burdensome pricing perspectives, the Langdale case study shows how it can be done and pay for itself many times over—including travel—in rural Georgia. *(Chapter 19, Case Study: Langdale Industries)*
Criminal abuse of the system	Mostly outside the domain of employers, however effective approaches make employees less vulnerable to pursuing illegal drugs.
Insurers' refusal to cover validated treatments	Health Rosetta type benefits pay for evidence-based services, such as physical therapy, cognitive behavioral therapy and other behavioral health services delivered via telehealth, value-based primary care, etc. *(Chapter 1; Chapter 5; Chapter 12; Chapter 13)*

Throughout this book, I have highlighted progressive employers and benefit strategies that have created replicable microcosms of high-performing health care as good as any in the world. It's in the enlightened self-interest of all employers to follow suit.

CONCLUSION

I often think about a question that should make us all step back a bit. Why are millennials—the largest American generation and current chunk of the workforce—the first generation to think life won't be better for them than their parents?[127] In a nation of optimists, this is worrisome at best. I've come to realize that the cost of health care is a primary underlying cause of their worry. Over half of their lifetime earnings are on track to go to health care.[128] As they have children and their indestructibility fades, millennials are realizing that they're going to be indentured servants to the health care system. This is profoundly sobering, but the good news is we've solved tougher problems and this one has already been solved in microcosms around the country.

Our health care system is overwhelming us, making too many of us lose hope. If I only accomplished one thing with this book, it would be to create hope in the simple, practical, proven fixes you've read here. Smart benefits programs make wise decisions free or near-free and bad decisions expensive. They don't just make all decisions expensive. At core, it's this simple. So-called experts (many of them my peers) who suggest it's more complicated are often so mired in today's wildly underperforming status quo that it obscures the simple solutions hidden in plain view. Plus, status quo protectors are quite adept at making health care far more complex than necessary.

As Dan Munro likes to say, "the [health care] system was never broken, it was designed this way."[129] The best way to describe the status quo payment system is a Gordian Knot designed by Rube Goldberg. Brain surgery *is* complex. Cancer *is* complex. Building a high performing health benefits plan doesn't need to be.

Perhaps the most common corporate platitude is "our employees are our greatest asset." If that's the case, status quo health benefits aren't exactly delivering a great ROI. Wise CEOs have realized this and that they operate a health care business, whether they like it or not. They also realize it's the last major P&L line item they haven't optimized or brought into the modern world. Over the last 20 years, employers have increased total employee payroll spending dramatically, yet most of us don't see the benefits because it has largely gone to health care benefits costs. Forward-looking employers are putting more money in their employees' pockets while delivering superior care, driving significant financial improvements, and creating a higher performance workforce

If it wasn't already clear, true fixes to our health care mess aren't coming from DC. As I write this, the latest attempt at "reform" by Congress is yet another example of rearranging deck chairs on the Titanic. Doubling down on paying into a "system" that has no correlation between price and value; and every single day causes 10,000 incidents of serious harm and hundreds of death from preventable medical mistakes is the definition of insanity.[130]

Hundreds of thousands of regular citizens, clinicians, CEOs, union leaders, and others are restoring the American Dream one community and company at a time. They're stepping up in grassroots groups and working together to solve the crisis. They're rallying around Health 3.0, Health Rosetta, the Right Care Alliance, the We the Patients movement, and many more. This is what America does. When it comes to big societal problems like civil rights, better food, or energy independence—we're best at solving these problems from the bottom up. The goal of this book and the Health Rosetta ecosystem is to simplify recreating these successes in your own community and across America. Let's get started.

5 Steps to Start Implementing High-Performance Benefits

Below are simple steps to start taking control of your benefits.* First, a few important reminders.

1. As much as half of your spending provides no value. Imagine allowing any other P&L line item to perform this poorly. It's unimaginable.
2. Technology, vendors, and service providers that can help remove this wasteful spending while improving your employees' health already exist. They can drive far better outcomes and lower costs, however most approaches aren't yet part of status quo health plans.
3. Favoring high performance vendors and services providers is a huge win for you and your employees. It also shifts the health care industry, helping solve our country's health care crisis.

The Health Rosetta ecossytem is certifying the people, products, services, and places that simplify adoption of successful approaches. We'll help you get started at healthrosetta.org.

With this in mind, here are 5 specific next steps you can and should take.

1. Reset your benefits advisor relationship expectations.

You deeply rely on your benefits advisor, consultant, or broker to navigate this complex world. In our experience, ~5% of the benefits brokers and consultants are worth their weight in gold. They have deep expertise and tremendous commitment to their clients' best interests. A litmus test for whether yours falls into this group is to ask them to complete and sign the compensation disclosure form in Appendix C. The high performers will have

---

* *Healthrosetta.org/employers has more resources, including a calculator to show the EBITDA impact of high-performance health benefits and the revenue you'd need to generate to create similar impact.*

no problem agreeing to this long before you make any benefits purchasing decisions. If they hesitate, make excuses, or refuse, this is a major red flag. I'd encourage you to find a high performance benefits advisor or consultant by following the guidance in Chapter 10.* You need someone on your side.

In tandem, evaluate the plan administrator you are working with. Chapters 13 and 17 address the shortcomings of many plan administrators and what you should expect from an optimal plan administrator.

2. Start now and select approaches that minimize disruption to your benefits group.

Don't be a slave to the annual benefits process. It's largely designed for a broker's or health plan's convenience, not your objectives. Many high-performance strategies can be implemented any time of the year. It often makes sense to do so off-cycle to manage your benefits group's workload.

3. Build compounding momentum by implementing programs that quickly reduce spending and deliver value.

Part IV of the book (Chapters 14-20) summarizes a few of the Health Rosetta's highest impact components. These components have proven themselves to deliver improved health outcomes and drive significant savings in relatively short time lines, usually within 12 months. They quickly free resources by addressing big ticket items like pricing failures, fraud, overtreatment, misdiagnosis, and drug spend.

Build support by positioning these programs to employees as new, better benefits, even if they are layered on top of your current plan design. Three simple examples that work for nearly any size organization and don't require geographically concen-

---

* *The Health Rosetta ecosystem certifies transparent, mission-aligned benefits advisors and others. Naturally, there are great advisors who aren't yet aware of this certification, so you might have one that isn't yet certified. However, we're doing the utmost to identify, accept, and hold accountable as many of the strongest performers as possible.*

trated workforces are pharmacy analysis/optimization, Centers of Excellence models, and out-of-network claims settlement services. I also recommend using some of the initial savings to fund further programs, as this compounds momentum.

You'll likely need help from a high-performance benefits advisor, but the Health Rosetta ecosytem can also help navigate this process. We'll even help find an advisor willing and able to drive the process.

4. Develop an outstanding communications strategy to ensure program success.

Companies typically fully transition their workforce to high-performance benefits over a couple years, creating compounding momentum each year. This requires strong employee communication.

A natural place to start is new employees and millennials. For example, you can default new employees into new, higher value benefits programs positioned as "Tier 1." You keep the old programs as "Tier 2" (see the case study on Enovation Controls after Chapter 14 to see how they did it). Word will spread and people will naturally transition to Tier 1. Millennials are often the early adopters of what everyone ultimately adopts. Health care's status quo is nearly a perfect polar opposite to what millennials want and value (e.g., convenience, transparency, etc.). See Chapter 4 on how to leverage millennials to transform your benefits.

Larger employers can also start with locales where they can phase in changes to work out kinks and ensure value is being delivered.

5. Let the Health Rosetta ecosystem help guide the way.

We can give you access to resources, insight, and people to help navigate the process. Your path and focus will vary significantly based on your organization type, size, geography, employee base, current plan, and more. We'll help you get the lay of the land, serving as a backstop against common myths and misinformation about what you can achieve.

Restore the American Dream for Your Community

Why did I write this book? In short, it became something I couldn't not do after seeing dozens of organizations that have reduced their spending by 20% or more *while* saving their employees from losing their health and financial solvency. They spend $2,000 to $5,000 less per member every year. These same results are possible for nearly any purchaser that has the will and access to the right expertise. This can go into your employee's pocket, business, and community. It's how you can personally help restore the American Dream.

Successes are sprouting up all over the country, from small manufacturers to school districts to publishers to large municipalities to Fortune 100 companies. If every employer adopts these common sense steps, we'll create a $500B citizen-driven economic stimulus every year while dramatically improving the lives of countless citizens.

However, there are $3 trillion reasons to protect health care's status quo. To stop progress, there's nothing easier to politicize, confuse, and frighten people with than health care. It's life and death, right?

Those looking to protect the underperforming status quo will try to politicize health care and use fear, uncertainty and doubt to protect their interests.

However, let's be clear about the stakes. Data from Rand, Brookings, Kaiser, Health Affairs, and other reputable sources have shown that hyperinflating health care costs have been 95% responsible for 20 years of income stagnation and decline for the middle class and our most vulnerable citizens. This has profoundly and negatively impacted nearly every single American. It's a national shame that we can reverse.

No industry spends anywhere near what health care does

on marketing and lobbying at the local, state and federal levels. Each of us must inoculate ourselves against status quo enablers who benefit—at the cost of our health and our wealth—when they infect us with the sense that health care is too complex to fix.

This is simply false and the Health Rosetta shows how and why. Hundreds have been coming together to create this free, open source blueprint that uses real life successes to show how health care isn't too complex to fix. For each major Health Rosetta component, it explains how it works, why it is better than the status quo, what challenges to expect, steps to take action, and links to more resources. We're just getting started with where we're taking it, but people and organizations representing millions of Americans are already jumping on board.

Americans are no longer waiting for solutions from somewhere else. We're looking in the mirror and realizing it's on us to restore the American Dream. The fixes even transcend the lines that divide us.

- In Pittsburgh, unions and management put aside old battles and rethought how to deliver great benefits to teachers. As a result, Pittsburgh kindergartners will have $2 billion more for education during their K-12 years than their counterparts in Philadelphia. Pittsburgh's teachers are also paid more, have better benefits, and have 30% smaller classes sizes.
- Successes are being created by people across the political spectrum. Progressives are implementing approaches that some would call conservative. Conservatives are implementing approaches that some would call progressive.

The common thread in each is that the people involved shifted their mindset, realizing that we don't need left-or-right, management-or-labor solutions. We need an American solution and the good news is it's spreading like wildfire.

No matter who you are, there's a way to take action.

- **Employees**. Share with your CEO, CFO, and benefits leader that they can slash health care costs while improving benefits.

- **Executives & Public Sector Leaders.** You can ignore so-called experts and apply the same discipline to purchasing health care as every other area of your organization.
- **Union Leaders.** There's never been a better time to rethink your relationship with management in regard to the health benefits costs that have been crushing your members. When it comes to health care, you're on the same side.
- **Clinicians & Health Care Professionals.** You and your organization can buck the status quo by embracing the Health 3.0 Vision and Health Rosetta Principles outlined in Appendices D to F. We'll even help. If your organization won't do it, go to an organization that will.
- **Every Other Citizen.** Persuade those in your community to take action by telling them about the Health Rosetta or giving them this book.

For too long, we've let health care crush the American Dream. We won't survive 20 more years of a middle class economic depression. No country has smarter or more compassionate nurses and doctors. No country has more innovators that have reinvented our country time and again. Nearly every individual in health care went into it for all the right reasons, but perverse incentives and outdated approaches have left them shackled or downtrodden. Whether we knew it or not, we all contributed to this mess. Now, it's on all of us to fix it. When change happens community by community, it's impossible to stop.

Yes, health care stole the American Dream. But it's absolutely possible to take it back. Join us to make it happen in your community.

APPENDIX A

DETAILED CASE STUDIES ON THE FAILURES OF WORKPLACE WELLNESS PROGRAMS

The following are more detailed case studies of the summaries we discussed in Chapter 8 about how workplace wellness programs consistently fail to achieve positive ROI. A special thanks to Al Lewis and Vic Khanna for the case studies.[131]

1. Reducing Cardiac Care Expenses by $100 Per Employee. Not.

The nation's leading workplace wellness program promoter is Watson Health's Ron Goetzel, senior scientist at Johns Hopkins Bloomberg School of Public Health and vice-President, Consulting and Applied Research at Truven Health Analytics. In the February 2017 issue of *Health Affairs*, Goetzel concluded that employers spend an average of $327 per employee per year (PEPY) on spending related to cardiac care.[132] He has said elsewhere that a good program costs a little less than half that, or $150 PEPY.[133] Essentially, he is saying that a program would need to reduce cardiac spending by almost 50 percent just to break even.

Given that most employees don't want to participate in such programs and rarely change behaviors if they do, that's going to be tough. But tough quickly morphs into impossible when you look deeper. Because Goetzel combined cardiac prevention spending (like tests, doctor visits, statins, etc.) with cardiac care spending on events (like heart attacks) to reach that $327 figure. Yet prevention spending and event spending are opposite types of expenses. Workplace wellness programs push employers to increase prevention spending to avoid event spending. Hence, they should vary inversely.

His asserted savings from a workplace wellness program evaporate if the two types of expenses are, quite appropriately, separated.[134] Peeling out heart attacks—a roughly 1-in-1000 shot in the working-age population, costing maybe $50,000 apiece—shows that most cardiac spending already goes to prevention, since heart attacks and related events cost only $50 PEPY. A perfect wellness program costing $150 would therefore lose around $100 PEPY.

2. Connecticut Wellness Program Increases Health Care Spending

We've all heard the saying "The operation was a success but the patient died." That's pretty much what happened in the state of Connecticut.

Analysts looking at outcomes for the state employee workplace wellness program concluded in a *Health Affairs* article[135] that it actually increased health care spending. But that was "a good thing," according to an interview with Connecticut Comptroller Kevin Lembo.[136]

Lembo also explained that costs increased because people are getting more checkups, which he calls "high-value care." However, checkups are far more likely to find problems that don't exist than to successfully address problems that do, according to *the Journal of the American Medical Association*.[137] The USPSTF and Consumer Reports Choosing Wisely program specifically says annual checkups "usually don't make you healthier."[138]

The same checkups were said to account for a drop of 10 percent in ER visits. Yet, the benefits plan's first-ever copay for ER visits ($35) was put in place during the same period, a far more likely cause for the drop.

Meanwhile, state employees are potentially being harmed. The Connecticut program requires female employees to get mammograms while they are still in their thirties. This is such a bad idea that the USPSTF guidelines don't even bother recommending against it. The rate of false-positives from routine mammography of young women—requiring biopsies and possibly even mastectomies—overwhelms the possibility of saving a life.

Connecticut didn't disclose how much its program costs, but assume the usual $100 to $150 PEPY. Then add on to that an undisclosed increase in health spending, plus the possibility of harming female employees, plus the lost work time for all those extra doctor visits and screens. This program could be costing state taxpayers hundreds of dollars per state employee.

3. The Wellness Trade Association's Official Guidebook Says Wellness Loses Money

Perhaps uniquely in the annals of trade associations in any industry, the Health Enhancement Research Organization (HERO) actually admits their members' product—workplace wellness programs—doesn't work. The tables, charts, and figures in this section are directly drawn from their *Program Measurement and Evaluation Guide: Core Metrics for Employee Health Management*, downloadable from the Population Health Alliance website.[139]

Specifically, the study highlighted by HERO shows that $0.99 per employee per month (PEPM) in savings stemming from "potentially preventable hospitalizations" are not enough to cover workplace wellness program expenses (Employee Health Management, or EHM), which they peg at an unrealistically economical $1.50 PEPM.

From page 15 of the Guidebook.

1,000	Number of members
45	Expected Hospitalizations/K
$25,000	All-in cost of a hospitalization
$1.50	Cost of EHM PMPM, fees

Then, from page 23, the $0.99 savings in "potentially preventable hospitalizations."

Savings estimate	
Trend: PPH	-17%
Trend: All-cause except PPH	-2%
Saved PPH/K	0.53
Saved PPH for population	9.26
Weighted cost/PPH	$22,500
Saved PPH cost	$208,393
Saved PPH cost PMPM	$0.99

One might say: "Yes, maybe avoidance of 'potentially preventable hospitalizations' doesn't cover the costs, but surely workplace wellness programs impact other costs." And they do—but the impacts go in the wrong direction. On page 22, HERO says that:

> [W]hile we focus on decreased impactible [sic] utilization here, it is important to recognize that EHM [employee health management] should increase the use of certain services, such as preventive and screening services, certain chronic medications, and outpatient visits. It is even possible to see a rise in ER and urgent care visits.

Critics would argue that even the $0.99 is overstated, by about the same amount, because the hospitalization rates that declined enough to generate that modest savings figure were related to asthma and heart attacks—and hospitalization rates for asthma and heart attacks were declining at about the same pace everywhere in the country, workplace wellness program or not.

4. The Wellness Industry Trade Publication Admits Multiple Wellness Failures

In its thirty-year history, the *American Journal of Health Promotion* (*AJHP*) has never once published an article showing losses from workplace wellness programs or criticizing them in any meaningful way—at least, not on purpose.

Their first slip-up came in an editorial in the September/October 2013 issue, when they admitted that 90 to 95 percent of programs have no impact.[140]

The second was when they published a meta-analysis showing that ROIs varied inversely with "methodological quality." In other words, badly measured studies showed high ROIs, while well-measured studies showed low ROIs.[141]

Among well-measured studies, the highest-quality studies of all are randomized control trials (RCTs), which are the "gold standard." For example, RCTs are required to get drugs approved. To their credit, the authors admitted that RCTs "exhibited negative ROI." But then, to nobody's credit, they concluded that ROIs were positive by averaging the ROIs from the invalid studies with the valid ones! In the same way that "averaging" Copernicus and Ptolemy leads to the conclusion that the earth revolves halfway around the sun.[142]

This was definitely a slip-up. A subsequent July/August 2014 *AJHP* issue devoted the entire "Editor's Notes" to explaining why they didn't really mean it, and really, "no one knows" what wellness ROI is.[143]

The third example was from that very same editor, Michael O'Donnell, who eventually gave up on finding an ROI in health care spending. "Who cares about an ROI anyway?" were his exact words.[144] Yes, forget about sales incentives, product enhancements, marketing, advertising, or social media. According to

O'Donnell, the surefire way to increase revenues—by 1 percent—is to pay your employees to exercise.

> To reflect the full value of goods and services produced by each employee, the 1% increase in productivity should reflect revenues earned per employee. For example, if total payroll costs represented 30% of total revenues, a 1% increase in productivity might really represent $1933 [in extra revenues] for an average employee.[145]

Mr. O'Donnell's cost accounting is as creative as his way of generating revenue. Somehow, in Mr. O'Donnell's calculation, no revenues are lost when employees are off the line, phones, trucks, or sales floor for 90 minutes a week (a 3.75 percent productivity drop in a 40-hour work week). Only the time itself is lost. He calculates this as $2,184. That, of course, exceeds the revenue increase, generating losses of $251 PEPY from lost work time. That is in addition to the usual $100+ PEPY loss from paying vendors.

These examples are hardly cherry-picked. They're legion. But just to be fair, let's look at what the industry itself says are the best programs.

The Industry's Supposed Best

The following vendors and programs were selected by a committee of workplace wellness program executives led by Ron Goetzel as the best of their respective years, each of them winning the industry's top Koop Award (named for former Surgeon General C. Everett Koop).

2011: Eastman Chemical

Between 2004 and 2006, Eastman Chemical apparently generated massive savings from a workplace wellness program before the program had even started, as Figure 13 shows. The upper line shows the cost trend for nonparticipants, the lower line for participants. Note that while both trend lines started out at roughly the same point, by 2006 the nonparticipants' line was

$2,432 while the participants checked in at $2,073, a "savings" of $359. On a side note, the risk factors for participants stayed almost the same between 2004 and 2008, meaning no savings could be attributable to the program even if it had existed the entire time.

Health Fitness Corporation/Eastman Chemical ROI Analysis from Koop Committee Submission

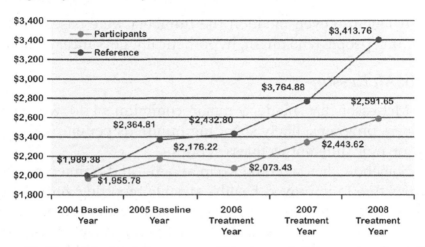

Figure 13. *The original and the suppressed X-axes can both be seen together, with a timeline connecting them at the link in the endnote.*[118] *Note, the above graphic is a replication of the original chart to improve readability.*

2012: State of Nebraska

The Nebraska program claimed to have saved the lives of 514 state employees with colon cancer. However, Al Lewis has pointed out that this would have been statistically impossible given that only a few thousand state employees (the state would not disclose the exact figure) were screened for colon cancer in the first place and only 5 percent of Americans will get colon cancer, 90 percent of them over age 50.[146] The medical director of the state's workplace wellness program vendor, Health Fitness Corporation, explained to the *Omaha World-Herald*[147] that what he meant when he said that the employees had cancer was that the employees didn't have cancer, but they could get it someday. Indeed, that is true—and not just for those 514 state employees but for everyone else as well.

As you can see, the actual report didn't address the medical director's nuance that the program didn't actually catch any cancer cases.

With its targeted messaging strategy, the State of Nebraska has helped catch 514 new cases of early stage cancer before it was too late![148]

It failed to even mention the numbers were based on just screening people who might, hypothetically, get cancer someday.

2015: McKesson

McKesson has made a major commitment to workplace wellness programs, likely spending hundreds per employee per year on nine different wellness vendors.

Somehow they won the Koop award—and claimed massive savings due to improved health—despite reporting zero change in employee health risk factors. Note that their total biometric risk factors did not fall. Instead, the "increased to elevated risk" column virtually offsets the entire "decreased to low risk" column.

Risk Factor	Stayed at low risk	Increased to elevated risk	Stayed at elevated risk	Decreased to low risk
BMI	25%	6.5%	64%	5.4%
Cholesterol	51%	13.1%	25%	10.5%
SBP	40%	15.6%	28%	16.7%
DBP	57%	12.6%	14%	17.1%
Glucose	73%	8.8%	11%	6.9%
Cotinine	87%	1.5%	9%	1.6%

Summary Table of 5,923 Improvements and 6,397 Deteriorations in Biometrics for Boise School District, Provided by Wellsteps (without Disclosing Totals)

2016: Boise School District

At least McKesson's employee risk factors didn't deteriorate. The same can't be said of the Boise School District and its workplace wellness program vendor, Wellsteps. Like McKesson and its vendors, they did not total the increases and decreases in risk factors. Deliberately or not, they also displayed them in a manner that obfuscated the total changes in each direction of risk.

Improvements and Deteriorations in Biometrics

	No.	Mean at Baseline	Mean Change through 1 year	F Test P Value
BMI (Kg/m^2)				
Normal (<25)	903	22.4	0.2	< 0.0001
Overweight (25.0-29.9)	738	27.2	0.1	
Obese (≥ 30.0)	683	35.2	-0.3	
Missing	62			
Systolic Blood Pressure (mmHg)				
Normal (<120)	906	110.9	10.9	< 0.0001
Pre-hypertensive (120-139)	1086	128.5	3.9	
High (140-159)	322	146.1	-3.7	
Dangerous (≥160)	38	167.3	-12.6	
Missing	59			
Diastolic Blood Pressure (mmHg)				
Normal (<80)	1330	71.2	1.8	< 0.0001
Pre-hypertensive (80-89)	778	83.8	-4.2	
High (90-99)	209	93.2	-8.7	
Dangerous (≥100)	33	105.6	-15.9	
Missing	61			
Glucose (mg/dL)				
Normal (<110)	2134	92.0	-2.9	< 0.0001
IFG (110-125)	117	115.1	-7.4	
Diabetes (≥126)	72	170.4	-27.1	
Missing	88			

Total CHL (mg/dL)				
Normal (<200)	1434	169.1	10.5	< 0.0001
Borderline (200-239)	691	215.6	-1.7	
High risk (≥240)	216	260.3	-14.6	
Missing	70			

Summary Table of 5,923 Improvements and 6,397 Deteriorations in Biometrics for Boise School District, Provided by Wellsteps (without Disclosing Totals)[149]

Once you parse the data, you see that employee health deteriorated in grand fashion, since 1004 more risk factors deteriorated than improved. This objective deterioration in risk mirrored the subjective deterioration. As the table below shows, employees actually *felt* that their health deteriorated over the period, from 7.96 to 7.92 on a scale of 10. If you're wondering why the awards committee honored Boise, consider the number of applicants in 2016, seven.[150]

Health Behavior and Emotional Health Outcomes over 2 Years (n=1,873)

Health Behaviors	Baseline	Year 1	Year 2	F	P
Exercise (d/wk)	3.34±1.40	3.42±1.35	3.50±1.34	11.20	<0.0001
Exercise (min/wk)	165.4±155.0	177.9±159.2	186.5±174.5	11.39	<0.0001
Fruits (serv/d)	2.38±1.15	2.49±1.18	2.54±1.20	20.09	<0.0001
Vegetables (serv/d)	2.70±1.20	2.81±1.22	2.81±1.19	10.90	<0.0001
Sleep (d/wk)	4.76±1.69	4.71±1.70	4.82±1.64	3.32	0.0361
Smoking (d/wk)	4.35±1.33	5.43±2.71	4.27±3.08	10.53	<0.0001

Alcohol (drinks/d)	1.31±0.72	1.16±0.79	1.10±0.79	30.00	<0.0001
Self-Rated Health	7.96±1.37	7.88±1.34	7.92+1.35	7.31	0.0007

One- and two-year improvements were seen in exercise, fruit and vegetable consumption, days or quality sleep, tobacco and alcohol use, and self-rated health.

Of course, massive savings were claimed. Read Figure 14 below carefully. When read in conjunction with the above deterioration of outcomes, it appears that the more health deteriorated, the greater the savings from wellness…until roughly a third of all health benefits expenses for the Boise School District were apparently wiped out by the program.[151]

Predicted versus Actual Medical Costs for the District

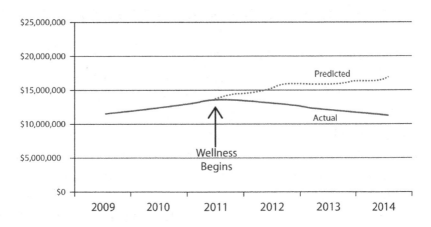

Figure 14. Predicted Versus Actual Medical Costs for the District.

APPENDIX B

CLIENT NOTICE, PLAN SPONSOR BILL OF RIGHTS, AND CODE OF CONDUCT

Sample Health Rosetta Client Notice

Congratulations! We're excited you've decided to work with a Health Rosetta Certified Benefits Professional. The Health Rosetta ecosystem's mission is to help group benefits purchasers sustainably reduce health benefits costs and provide better care for their employees. We maintain the Health Rosetta, an expert-sourced blueprint for wisely purchasing benefits sourced from the highest-performing benefits purchasers and experts every-where.

A primary goal of Helath Rosetta certification programs is to help benefits purchasers reduce your spending *while* improving the quality of care your plan members receive. This notice is to help you understand what to expect working with a Health Rosetta Certified Benefits Professional.

What to Expect?

One of our core principles is that higher transparency, trust, and integrity in the purchasing process improves the quality of benefits purchasing decisions. To facilitate this, HRI certified professionals commit in our agreement with them to adhere to certain specific practices.

- Only make changes that have been shown to improve care while improving your costs AND your employees' costs. No more choosing between hurting you or hurting your employees.
- Review this notice with you to set expectations.
- Fully and meaningfully disclosure their compensation in writing.
- Think, plan, and act in your long-term interests, including completing 3-5 year strategic plans.
- Adhere to the HRI Code of Conduct you should have received with this notice
- Adhere to the HRI Plan Sponsor Bill of Rights you should have receive with this notice.

These practices significantly differentiate both certified professionals and their design, purchasing, and management process from the highly-conflicted, opaque status quo process. To maintain the quality of HRI certification programs, they'll ask you to sign this notice and a couple other documents throughout the purchasing process.

How the Health Rosetta Ecosystem and Certification Benefit You

You'll likely benefit both directly and indirectly as a result of working with a HRI certified benefits professional. Here are a couple of the main ways.

- **Higher-value benefits** – You should start seeing returns in the form of sustainably lower costs and higher quality care within the next 12 months. While we can't promise specifics as this varies on many factors, Health Rosetta components implemented by other employers have sustainably reduced their spending by 10-40% per year.
- **Access to a deep ecosystem of solutions and best practices** – Our health care system is in the early days of a dramatic transformation, with many new innovative approaches. This makes it difficult for you and most advisors to see through the noise. Certified professionals have access to other certified people, industry leading experts, the Health Rosetta blueprint, and other community resources to sift through this, improving the likelihood that design changes, programs, technologies, and services you implement are appropriate and likely to work.
- **Learning from others** – The education and other resources we make available for certified professionals are based on the real life experience of other purchasers, not theory. We actively cultivate shared learning to keep us abreast. We maintain a network of more than 3,500 experts and high national visibility to create a hivemind for identifying the best approaches. See just a few of our collaborators at healthrosetta.org/who-we-are/.

We have high expectations for certified professionals and work to attract those seeking to go above and beyond them. However, if you feel your certified professional is not meeting your needs, discuss with them or contact us directly at employers@healthrosetta.org. . We're happy to help. You can find more resources, our book *The CEO's Guide to Restoring the American Dream*, and subscribe to updates and education at healthrosetta.org.

From Dave, Sean, and the entire Health Rosetta team, we'd like to thank you for choosing to work with a HRI Certified Professional.

Health Rosetta Plan Sponsor Bill of Rights

1. Service Agreement Fiduciary Duty Protection

You have the right to ensure that your obligations as your plan's sponsor, administrator and fiduciary are protected and enhanced in your service agreement.

2. Transparent Relationships & Conflict Disclosure

You have the right to expect transparency, including disclosure of conflicts, in financial dealings between you and your broker, advisor, or consultant, carriers, and vendors.

3. Independence

You have the right to ensure those financial dealings do not compromise your fiduciary responsibility and the independence of the advice you receive.

4. Access to all options

You have the right to receive information about the full range of options available to you, not just those which preserve or optimize your representative's income or plan administrator's revenue.

5. Independent Review

You have the right to an unbiased, independent review of all pertinent market options in an impartial manner, not just those which preserve or optimize your representative's income or plan administrator's revenue.

6. Comprehensive Reporting

You have the right to receive comprehensive reporting of your costs, and the potential drivers of those costs.

7. Answers to Questions

You have the right to receive answers to your questions, with no cloaking of responses with HIPAA Privacy and other "confidentiality" curtains.

8. Effective Adjudication

You have the right to expect those you hire to adjudicate benefits to give their best effort to identifying inappropriate and grossly inflated charges before they issue payment.

9. Access to data

You have the right to your data and should agree upon this requirement prior to execution of any vendor agreement.

10. Complete reporting

You have the right to receive complete service and outcome reporting from each of your vendors, including all fees associated with services rendered.

Health Rosetta Benefits Advisor Code of Conduct

Good for employees and employers

We resolve to only implement programs and solutions that seek to improve the plan sponsor's bottom line, the plan member's bottom line, and most importantly, the plan member's health.

Programs should do no harm

We resolve that brokers, consultants, and advisors should do no harm to employee health, corporate integrity, or employee/employer finances. Instead we will endeavor to support employee well-being for our customers, their employees and all program constituents.

Employee Benefits and Harm Avoidance

We will only recommend implementing programs with/ for employees rather than to them, and will focus on promoting responsible practices for the health plans we serve.

Our choices of programs and strategies shall always prioritize best outcomes at the lowest cost, in that order, with a strong focus on the responsibility that an employer should provide affordable coverage for their employees while respecting the financial integrity of the business.

Respect for Corporate Integrity and Employee Privacy

We will not share employee-identifiable data with employers and will ensure that all protected health information (PHI) adheres to HIPAA regulations and any other applicable laws.

Commitment to Transparency

Our focus shall be to bring transparency to all levels of health care financing. From how we get paid to how insurance companies and PBMs get paid to how providers get paid.

Commitment to Valid Outcomes Measurement

Our contractual language and outcomes reporting will be transparent and plausible. The end goal is to improve outcomes and quality of care while lowering costs and the ability to do this shall be measured and reported on in a valid, consistent and accountable format.

SAMPLE COMPENSATION DISCLOSURE FORM

The following is a sample broker compensation disclosure form to help you improve your benefits purchasing process. The status quo is rife with conflicts of interest stemming from undisclosed compensation arrangements. This prevents benefits purchasers from making the most informed and intelligent purchasing decisions. We've found that the first step towards high-performance benefits is disclosure of incentives to minimize conflicts, create transparency, and increase trust in your advisors and process.

Calculation of Fees

In general, each fee should be calculated in one of five ways.

1. **Premium based.** Fees are based on the amount of premium for each line of coverage. This normally expressed as a predetermined percentage.
2. **Claims-based.** Fees are based on the $ amount or number of claims in the plan and generally are expressed as percentages or aggregate per claim fees for the period.

3. **Per member, eligible, or employee (e.g. PEPM/PMPM).** Fees are based upon the number of eligible employees or actual members in the plan.
4. **Transaction-based**. Fees are based on the execution of a particular plan service or transaction.
5. **Flat rate**. Fees are a fixed charge that does not vary, regardless of plan size

You can also access a regularly updated digital version on the Health Rosetta website (healthrosetta.org).

HEALTH ROSETTA
BENEFITS REPRESENTATIVE COMPENSATION DISCLO-
SURE FORM

Advisor: _____   Client: _____   Period: _____

Overview

A key element of the Health Rosetta ecosystem's mission is to help benefits purchasers build transparent, trusted relationships with benefits advisors that are critical to an effective benefits-purchasing process, particularly in today's world of skyrocketing health care costs and limited ability to push those costs on employees. This form is one resource to help you.

Their compensation is a small portion of total spend, but the right one can guide the way to dramatically improving your plan costs and quality. The total amount shouldn't be the primary focus. Instead, it should help build trust and identify potential conflicts.

High-value, forward-leaning advisors are worth their weight in gold. Plus, the strategies they use typically improve your bottom line, reduce your employees' out-of-pocket spending, and improve the quality of care they receive. Think of it this way.

Would you rather pay 4 percent to an advisor who reduces total spending by 15 percent or 2 percent to one who "negotiates" a 15 percent increase down to a 7 percent increase? For every 100 employees on an average plan, you'd save $247,220 in year 1 and $1.2 million in 5 years (net of the higher compensation).

Unwillingness to disclose compensation is typically a red flag that recommendations may not align with your interests. The benefits world often has undisclosed conflicts and incentives that make intelligent purchasing decisions difficult. To help you get around this, we've created a free guide for selecting high-value advisors.

You can find more resources or contact us at healthrosetta. org to learn more about improving the cost and quality of your health plan, Certified Professionals, or how we help benefits purchasers. A special thanks to Eric Krieg at Risk International Benefits Advisory, David Contorno at Lake Norman Benefits, Josh Jeffries at Arkin Youngentob Associates, and Tom Emerick at Edison Health for helping create this form. Each is a worth their weight in gold type.

About Us: The Health Rosetta's mission is to help public and private employers and unions sustainably reduce health benefits costs and provide better care for the 150 million Americans who access care through their work. We accelerate adoption of practical, nonpartisan fixes to health care's root causes of dysfunction—how we pay for care. We maintain the Health Rosetta, a blueprint for wisely purchasing benefits sourced from the highest-performing benefits purchasers and experts everywhere.

Overview of Services Provided

Some fees may be estimates and will vary throughout the course of the year. However, this shouldn't vary significantly from estimates unless something significant and unplanned happens.

Service Provided	External Vendor	Cost/ Fee for Service	Compensation Type	Total Compensation
Core Consulting Services				
Pharmacy Consulting Services				
Actuarial Services				
Compliance Services				
Wellness Consulting				
Claims Audit				
Data Analytics and Clinical Services				
Communications				
Decision Support Services & Transparency Resources				
Benefits Administration				
Total Projected Annual Costs				

Expected Financial Compensation from External Vendors

Category	Vendor	Effective Date	Compensation Type	Total Compensation
Medical				
Rx				
Dental				
Vision				

Stop loss				
EAP				
FSA				
Group Life				
AD&D				
LT Disability				
ST Disability				
Cancer				
Critical Illness				
Wellness				
Disease Mgmt.				
Broker Fee				
Other				
Total				

Are any compensation multipliers or other bonuses applicable to the above categories of compensation?
☐ Yes (please describe below)   ☐ No

If yes, are they included in the above dollar amounts?
☐ Yes   ☐ No

Do you or your firm accept any nonaccount specific financial compensation from any products, services, or vendors you're recommending, including, but not limited to, contingent or bonus commissions, override or retention bonuses, and back-end commissions.
☐ Yes (please describe below)   ☐ No

Do you or your firm have any other financial or nonfinancial compensation, potential conflicts of interest, or incentives related to products, services, or vendors you're recommending, including, but not limited to, ownership, equity stakes, revenue/profit

sharing, GPO/coalition participation, preferred vendor panels, conferences or trips, or personal relationships.
☐ Yes (please describe below)　　☐ No

Are there any potential reasons that could result in the above costs of services or compensation to vary more than 10 percent from the above projections?
☐ Yes (please describe below)　　☐ No

Please describe details related to any questions to which you answered yes above, including the specific, expected, or estimated dollar value. Attach additional pages if necessary.

Total Expected Compensation

Consulting Services	
Compensation from External Vendors	
Cost of Services from External Vendors	

Advisor
I certify that to the best of my knowledge the above is a complete and meaningful disclosure of my firm's entire compensation.

Client
I acknowledge that the signed Certified Advisor has presented and adequately reviewed the above disclosures.

Name: _____
Entity: _____
Title: _____
Signed:_____
Date _____

Name: _____
Entity: _____
Title: _____
Signed: _____
Date _____

APPENDIX D

HEALTH ROSETTA PRINCIPLES

The Health Rosetta Principles were created and curated with Leonard Kish. We drew these insights from dozens of the most forward-looking individuals in the health care industry. The Health Rosetta components in part IV of the book speak to how health care purchasers can be wise about their health care purchasing. The Health Rosetta Principles speak to how the health care industry should respond to changing purchasing and patient behavior to navigate uncharted terrain. They are the guide for how the industry can succeed in the future health ecosystem. Leading experts have written essays on specific principles that we invite you to read at healthrosetta.org/health-rosetta-principles. The essays expand on each principle to make them more actionable. In the open source spirit of the Health Rosetta, we invite other leading thinkers to contribute their essays to advance the cause.

A New Medical Science

1. *A New Paradigm* – A new social, psychological, biological, and information-driven medical science is emerging that will better understand a person's environmental context and its rela-

tionship with disease. It's precision medicine, but more, using sensors and networks to better predict and prevent as well as treat the root causes of disease. No vision of the future of medicine can be complete or even competent if it doesn't recognize these new sources of information and the power of patient engagement.

2. *Open source and open knowledge* – Open source, open APIs, open data, and open knowledge (such as wikis) will become central to defining a common architecture to support this new science. These are modern versions of peer review.

3. *Nonclinical determinants of outcomes* – To improve care and reduce costs with this new science, we must focus on what drives 80 percent of outcomes, the nonclinical factors, which include social, economic, and psychological determinants of health.

4. *Cross-disciplinary collaboration* – Cross-disciplinary collaboration and sharing of research data will be a requirement to accelerate new discoveries.

5. *Evidence-Based understanding of what works* – This new science will arrive at an evidence-based understanding of what works through a great wealth of shared longitudinal health data captured through mobile devices, sensors, and health records. It must be mindful of the concept of transforming data to information, knowledge, and wisdom.

6. *Understanding the personome* – The new medical science will focus on understanding the personome. "The influence of the unique circumstances of the person—the personome—is just as powerful as the impact of that individual's genome, proteome, pharmacogenome, metabolome, and epigenome."[152]

Openness Drives Effective Action

7. *Individual choice* – Individuals have the right to make choices and control their health destiny with the best information available.

8. *Open access to information* – Open access to information that will enable individuals to make the best decisions and become well-informed individuals, particularly when curated and contextualized by clinicians.

9. *Openness and privacy are not in conflict* – Openness and privacy are not in conflict with the right kinds of identity, consent, and data control mechanisms in place.

10. *A required culture change* – This openness will come with a required culture change. We must release information in order to ensure high-quality information and code. In software, Linus' Law states, "Given enough eyeballs, all bugs are shallow." Keeping information sealed until it is perfect will mean we miss opportunities to improve the data and fix the system.

Economics and Transparency

11. *Information asymmetries* – Information asymmetries lead to inefficient systems and suboptimal outcomes. Access to life-saving, taxpayer-supported research must be open.

12. *Social determinants of health* – Health and wealth are tightly linked. Eventually, poor financial health will negatively impact overall health.

13. *Cost as comorbidity* – The cost of care can be a comorbidity. By ignoring costs in clinical decisions, conditions can worsen as financial stress may drive individuals to choose not to follow a plan of care because it is too expensive.

14. *Individual's right to know the cost of care* – Individuals have the right to know how much care will cost before receiving care, both out of pocket and covered. When there is unpredictable complexity (not caused by medical error, which shouldn't be charged for at all), individuals should be informed of the most likely ranges.

15. *Personal responsibility* – Individuals have personal responsibility to manage their lives along with their care.

Relationships and Peer to Peer Networks Will Become Central

16. *Communication as medical instrument* – The most important "medical instrument" is communication. Communications drive actions, build relationships, and create trust.

17. *Data liquidity for improving health* – Exchange of personal health data will become enabled via decentralized Peer to Peer (P2P) networks and "HIEs of 1." These P2P exchanges will improve health literacy, healthy action, and a functioning health economy.

18. *P2P networked conversations* – P2P networked conversations will empower new ways of organizing better health, allowing individuals to "organize without organizations" (h/t Clay Shirky) for better care.

19. *Individuals and health research* – Verifiable, but deidentified, opt-in health data will become part of a unified view of health care for research and risk assessment. Individuals will have the choice to contribute.

New Intelligence

20. *Cognification* – To "Cognify" (h/t Kevin Kelly) is to instill intelligence into something. Medical knowledge will increasingly be "cognified" into the IoT and much of the world around us is made "smart" and data-aware. This is good, and will free people to care for themselves where they want to receive care.

21. *Feedback* – All feedback has utility. Whether the news is good or bad, opinions become known and become a source for improvement and competitiveness.

Community-driven Health

22. *Stewarding social and economic factors* – True health system leadership comes from not just being stewards of hospitals

and clinics but stewarding social and economic factors and the physical environment of a community, which account for half of outcomes.

23. *Partnering for community health* – Assessing community health needs and adopting strategies to address those needs will provide hospitals with a valuable opportunity to partner with community partners to identify strategies for improving health, quality of life, and the community's vitality.

24. *Building health literacy and community* – Health care organizations that aggressively promote health literacy will build community capacity in addressing health issues. This may mean enabling and curating others in the community to reach all facets of the community.

25. *Health and financial literacy* – Start by teaching medicine and psychological self-awareness and resilience to kids. Starting in schools, health education needs to include the "medicine" we consume every day. Insurance/benefits literacy should be included in schools' financial literacy courses.

26. *School lunches* – School lunches are an access point of great power: they reinforce or remove the unhealthy products we consume.

27. *"Let food be thy medicine"* – Hippocrates said, "Let food be thy medicine and medicine be thy food." Individuals are "poisoning" themselves by the food they eat, largely without knowing it.

28. *"Walking is man's best medicine."* – Hippocrates also said, "Walking is man's best medicine." Communities and workplaces that make it easy to walk and be active can gain an advantage over the status quo.

29. *Health care waste: A bandit stealing from our future* – Health care waste is like a bandit stealing from our future. Health care is breaking U.S. schools. Money once directed to education is getting gobbled up by health care's hyperinflation. This piles onto the problem that kids don't learn enough about health, nutrition, finance, or any of the things that lead to healthy, long lives.

New Choices for Individuals and Care Teams

30. *Health isn't limited to the clinic* – Health is not the limited time individuals spend in clinics. What happens in the other 99+ percent of their life has the greater impact on an individual's overall well-being.

31. *Better choices through motivation* – We will learn how to rapidly enable better choices through motivation, tools, and access to better choices and lifestyles. Each individual will respond differently, requiring a whole new level of personalization.

32. *Understanding motivations and habit change* – People are complicated with both innate drives and ingrained habits that work against long-term health. The psychology of understanding these motivations and habit change is critical to success in achieving better health.

33. *Wisdom of the individual* – Still, people will make incredibly smart decisions when they understand the true risks and choices.

34. *Mental health* – Mental health is an equal component of a person's overall health. Mental health directly impacts our physical health and our ability to recover from disease or medical interventions. Therefore, mental health needs to be deliberately and systematically integrated into the general health care system.

35. *Nutritional and environmental causes of disease* – Open information and research are needed to understand the nutritional and environmental causes of disease.

36. *Unhealthy food* – Foods that are void of nutrition are the tobacco of this generation.

37. *Optimizing health* – We have defined sick care very well: what happens when things go wrong and how to correct them. We have very little understanding of how to keep things going right, how to get people back on track when they go off the rails, nor how to continually optimize health. Innovations in research are changing this; new entrants will figure out how to enable it.

38. *Preventing the need for care* – Systems will be designed so individuals can stay healthy and take as few drugs, have as few procedures, and avoid the system as much as possible by engaging in self-care.

39. *Embracing the "flat world" of care* – The emergence of a flat world opens up new avenues to innovation about what has worked in other cultures. The US has the opportunity to learn to be open to ways of health care that originate outside our borders, particularly those that are more appropriate to the underserved.

Individuals and Engagement

40. *Inclusivity with individuals and caregivers* – Individuals and their caregivers are the greatest untapped sources of information, knowledge, and motivation. Optimizing care means partnering with individuals and caregivers to empower them.

41. *Experience had a "Triple Aim" too* – The effectiveness of engagement is tightly aligned with how convenient it is; how easily it integrates with where we live, work and play; how culturally relevant it is; and cost-effectiveness it is.

42. *Leveling the empowerment playing field* – Engagement and empowerment are different. Individuals are often most engaged, but least empowered. A partnership between individuals and clinicians is when health is optimized.

43. *"Patient engagement" is backwards* – "Patient engagement" is valuable, but backwards. Individuals need the health system to be engaged with them regularly, and not just during visits.

44. *"Individual centered" engagement* – An engaged individual is very different from "patient engagement" (h/t Gilles Frydman). One is individual centered, one is health system-centered. Achieving full health is the goal, not engaging with the health system.

45. *Engagement for avoiding the health system* – An individual can be engaged with their own health without entering the health system at all (h/t Hugo Campos). The goal of an individual is

often to become/stay free of the health care system. Engaging means empowering them to do so.

New Economics

46. *Choose wisely* – Choose wisely. Oftentimes, less is more.
47. *Prevention* – Oftentimes, early is better than late.
48. *Overtreatment* – Overtreatment is one of health care's greatest challenges. In many cases no treatment is much better than treatment.
49. *Sustainability* – A system that profits more from people with "problems" than those without and has a default set at "treat more" is destined to collapse due to its inherent unsustainability.
50. *Evidence-based care delivery* – Systems will become better aligned to better prevent overtreatment and undertreatment, driven by individual's access to information, informed by statistics.
51. *Empowering a patient to make rational economic choices* – Individuals enter the health care system to get measurements; to be diagnosed; and to seek answers, treatment and learn. Individuals will seek alternatives outside of expensive, inconvenient care centers. This will drive positive overall change in the health system.

New Education

52. *Scaling medical education for the future* – Medical education will be made continuous, engaging, and scalable in the age of increasing clinical demands and limited work hours.
53. *New approaches to learning* – Medical educators will make thoughtful use of technology and learning design. Those that excel will learn how MOOCs, community engagement, social media, simulation, and virtual reality might change the face of medical education.

54. *Harnessing the data deluge* – The flood of new medical information is impossible to keep up on for any one person. Physicians and other care providers will be enabled by better systems for filtering what's valuable for an individual's care.

55. *Rapid evolution* – Effective medical education must and will evolve rapidly to focus on care delivery and the use of digital tools in care delivery.

56. *Physician as community manager* – Medical education will recognize that because only 10–20 percent of health outcomes are driven by clinical care, physicians must also be stewards of community transformation. Physicians are in the best position to be good partners within a multidisciplinary alliance enabling community transformation.

New Data Ownership Rights

57. *Individual Rights* – An individual's access to and management of data about him/herself is a fundamental human and property right. Why is it easier to have your medical data hacked than for you to get access to it? (h/t Eric Topol)

58. *Monopolies* – Monopolies on medical knowledge and information are unethical.

59. *Single Patient Record* – Now that all information can be connected all the time, there should be only one record of health data that comes from an individual, controlled by the individual. Problems with HIPAA and "information blocking" are symptoms of a broken, pre-Internet, paper-driven era.

60. *Property Rights in a Distributed System* – Platforms will be developed to enable the rights and transactions around health data property. These platforms will be decentralized, yet enabled to focus on the individual in an instant. Be prepared.

61. *Patients Right to Data About Them* – Individuals have a right to any data that comes from a measurement of an internal state of their body, including medical devices.

62. *Immediacy of Access to Health Data* – Individuals have literally died, waiting for their lab data. An individual's lab and other

data should be made accessible to individuals as soon as it is available.

63. *Data Doesn't Cause Medical Harm* – Medical regulations exist to protect individuals from medical harm. Data, ideas, and information in the hands of individuals causes no medical harm.

64. *Safe Access to Data Without a Doctor's Permission* – Individual may have access to metrics and analysis about their own body without a doctor's permission as long as accessing that data poses no significant medical risk.

65. *Right to Privacy* – Individuals have a right to health data privacy. Rights to sharing must be established with the individual it originates from, or their legal agent, in advance of sharing.

66. *Health Information Anti-Discrimination* – Health data collected about an individual cannot be used to determine a person's access to capital (credit ratings), employment, education, housing, or health care services. This will be legislated and empowered by new technologies.

New Roles and Relationships for Providers

67. *Misaligned Incentives Impair Providers* – Misaligned reimbursement schemes have impaired providers from doing the primary job of healing and have often robbed them of their humanity. Paying for value will help them get the job of healing back.

68. *Enlightened Providers Partner with Patients Who Guide Their Care* – The enlightened clinicians who embrace these guiding principles, combined with empowered individuals guiding their own care will become a powerful competitive advantage.

69. *Maintain Trust in Health Professionals* – Some of the most trusted professions are nurses, doctors, and pharmacists. With the trust individuals have in these professions, they activate us to do things we wouldn't normally do. Respect this trust.

70. *Whole-Person View of Health* – World class teams require a holistic view of a person's complete health, which includes not just their physical health but also their mental health.

71. *Embracing the Science of Behavior Change* – Relationships are fuel for motivation and behavior change (both positive and negative). Motivations, triggers, and ease of action are keys to enabling behavior change.

72. *The Importance of Relationships* – Aim to motivate, teach, consult, and enable. Clinicians cannot expect participation in a care plan (e.g., "adherence") without mutual understanding. Recognize that when an individual is not incapacitated, they are in control of whether they fill prescriptions, follow a care plan, etc.

73. *Health care Extends Beyond the Walls of the Clinic* – The best care is and will be collaborative beyond the walls of any one institution. Just as "the smartest people work for someone else," the smartest providers practice outside of this clinic and this hospital. The smartest provider may, in fact, be a collective, or the crowd. New ways to open communications will drive better care.

74. *Flipping the Clinic* – Many times, the best place for interaction between the clinician and an individual isn't at the clinic. We can flip the clinic. Much of what has been done at a clinic visit can be done more effectively in the comfort of an individual's home via email and other digital tools or in social settings like churches or community organizations.

75. *Embracing Data to Deliver Better Care* – The most relevant providers will learn and will be conversant in data analytics and tools. They will be experts in care delivery, not just diagnostics and traditional medical science.

A New Competition in Life Science & MedTech

76. *Embracing the New Science Within the Leadership* – Tomorrow's leaders will redesign development and trials to capitalize on

the aforementioned new science dynamics and mobile technologies.

77. *Embracing Partnerships Beyond the Traditional Ones* – New and nonobvious partnerships will need to be forged to ensure leadership in the future. Alliances with health tech and consumer health/Internet companies will be as important as alliances with academic medical centers have been in the past.

78. *Broadening the Value of PostTrial Relationships* – Posttrial relationships with individuals will allow cocreation and insights not possible before. That is a largely untapped opportunity. ResearchKit is just the beginning.

79. *Openness to Engagement* – The individual's relationship to a device or therapeutic may be as profound as their relationship to their doctor, or more so. Be available and open to engagement to make improvements.

New Health Plans, New Health Benefits

80. *Fee for Service Is Dying* – Fee for service is dying. Transition now in every way you can.

81. *The Dirty Secret of Health Plans* – The dirty secret of health plans is that higher care costs have, counterintuitively, led to greater profits for the plans. This is changing. Winning health plans will capitalize on the opportunity to fundamentally rethink plan design to be optimized for the fee-for-value era.

82. *Catalyzing Patient Engagement* – Catalyzing patient engagement will lead to better care and a more competitive offering.

83. *The Next Dirty Secret* – The next dirty secret of health plans is that they are money managers. The longer they hold onto money, the more they make. Employers and unions are driving the next wave of health care innovation, protecting their employees and members.

84. *Investing in Members' Financial Security* – Rather than reflexively denying claims and building up a mountain of ill will, insurance companies should invest resources in protecting their member's financial security.

85. *The "Negaclaim"* – Customers will, in effect, "self-deny" their own claims. A new metric for success is the "Negaclaim"—an unnecessary claim avoided. This isn't about denying care. Just as energy consumers aren't interested in kilowatt hours, individuals aren't interested in health claims—they want health restored and diseases prevented.

86. *True Informed Consent* – When individuals are fully educated on the trade-offs associated with interventions, they generally choose the less invasive approach.

87. *"Essential Access," the Corollary to "Essential Benefits"*—The ACA defined "essential benefits" but there will be a corollary about rights to "essential access" as part of coverage. Any modern health plan offering will include virtual visits, transparent price info, updated provider directory, same day e-mail response, next day test results, etc.—all eminently doable with today's modern technology.

88. *Rethinking Benefits Design and Procurement* – As the second or third biggest expense after payroll, CFOs & CEOs are failing in their fiduciary responsibility by being overly passive in how they procure health benefits. A rethought health care purchasing plan drives direct, financial returns, but most importantly, enables your valued employees to do what they desire—realize their full potential. Elements are defined at healthrosetta.org.

89. *Aligning Laboratory Testing and Genomics* – Genomics and proteomics information and testing will be key components of personalized medications, tailored to provide the best dose/response relationship in each patient. Because of their importance, these tests and genomic information must be covered by health plans and insurance.

New Health System

90. *Transitioning Care Beyond the Walls of the Clinic* – Hospitals have provided amazing service for the last 100 years, but location is becoming less important for health care. Care can

happen almost anywhere at lower cost. What conditions hospitals treat, and how hospitals serve their communities will dramatically change over the coming decades.

91. *Reimagining Technology in the Fee-for-Value Era* – Health systems, your technology procurement process must be up to the task. Systems grown and optimized for the waning fee-for-service often have the polar opposite design to what will optimize the fee-for-value era. Virtually every new health care delivery organization that is outperforming on Triple Aim objectives, has deployed new technology reimagined for the fee-for-value era.

92. *Focusing on Communication Over Billing* – Outside of health care, millions of organizations have reformulated how they interact with their ultimate customers with better communications tools. Next generation health care leaders understand that tools will focus on communication over billing.

93. *Borrowing a Page from the Newspaper Industry* – Health system leaders, learn from the another local oligopoly in your community, the venerable daily newspaper. While they spent the last couple of decades worrying about cross-town and traditional media company competition, it was death-by-a-thousand-papercuts that has been their undoing. Newspaper executives dismissed an array of new asymmetric competitors including eBay, Craigslist, Monster.com, Cars.com, Facebook, Groupon, ESPN, CBS Marketwatch and more who stole advertising, media consumption or both. Health system executives are doing the same thing today, and the issue is the same: how valuable content will be delivered in the future. The content is different, but the issue of distribution is the same.

94. *The "Forgotten" Fourth Aim* – Winning health care delivery organizations recognize that the Quadruple Aim will deliver sustainable success. The "forgotten aim" is a better experience for the health professional. Layering more bureaucracy on top of an already-overburdened clinical team ignores that the underlying processes are frequently underperforming and that a bad professional experience negatively impacts patient outcomes.

95. *Unshackling Innovation* – Health care organizations wanting to reinvent can harness the new opportunities by unshackling their smart, innovative team members and outside thinkers to reinvent their organizations for the next 100 years. Those that enable their customers will emerge as the leaders for the next 100 years.

HEALTH 3.0 VISION

> "Healthy citizens are the greatest asset any country can have."
> — Winston S. Churchill

As health benefits get a major overhaul in the employer arena and policymakers determine where publicly paid health care programs will go, we believe it's imperative to take a fresh look at how we've organized our health care "system." One area of near-universal agreement is that we should expect far more from our health care system, given the smarts, money, and passion poured into health care. Simply shifting who pays for care does little to address the underlying dysfunction of what we pay for and how we pay.

A group of forward-looking individuals have developed a vision for Health 3.0 to address the future of care. It is a common framework to guide the work of everyone from clinical leaders to benefits professionals to technologists to policymakers. Each should ask whether their strategies, technologies, and policies accelerate or hinder the journey to Health 3.0. If Health 3.0 is the North Star, the Health Rosetta is the roadmap and travel tips on how to get there.

To fix health care, we need a common vision for the future—Health 3.0 We believe this vision encompasses four key dimensions.

1. Health services (e.g. care delivery and self-care)

What is the optimal way to organize health services so they build on the strengths of each piece of the health puzzle, rather than operating as an unmatched set of pieces (today's world)? Innovative new care delivery models create a bright future (that some are already experiencing) where every member of the care team is operating at the top of his or her license and is highly satisfied with his or her role—a stark contrast to Health 2.0, where only 27 percent of a doctor's day is spent on clinical facetime with patients.[153] Put simply, they didn't go to med school to become glorified billing clerks.

2. Health care purchasing

Underlying virtually every dysfunction in health care is perverse economic incentives. Various industry players are acting perfectly rationally when they do things that are counterproductive to achieving Health 3.0. The Health Rosetta and Health 3.0 outline the high-level blueprint for how to purchase health and wellness services wisely. We've seen how a workforce can achieve what one health care innovator has described as "Twice the health care at half the cost and ten times the delight."

3. Enabling technology

Technology only turbocharges a highly functional organizational process when the proper organization structure, economic incentives, and processes are in place. Unfortunately, health care breaks the first rules I learned as a new consultant fresh out of school—don't automate a broken process and don't throw technology on top of a broken process. Sadly, health care is riddled with these two common mistakes, stemming from the flawed assumption that technology alone can be a positive force for change.

4. Enabling government

At the local, state, and federal level, government can play a tremendously beneficial (or detrimental) role in ensuring health care reaches its full potential. There are four main ways that government entities contribute.

1. As an enabler of health (e.g., public health and social determinants of health)
2. As a benefits purchaser, since government entities are large employers who can accelerate acceptance of new, higher-performing Health 3.0 care models
3. As a payer of taxpayer-funded health plans
4. As a lawmaking or regulating entity

The first item, in particular, is frequently overlooked as a powerful tool for testing and refinement of new models of care payment and delivery.

Failings of Health Care 1.0 and 2.0

Before defining Health 3.0 further, it's important to outline the failings of Health care 1.0 and 2.0. Dr. Zubin Damania (aka ZDoggMD) describes the positive facets of Health care 1.0 and Health care 2.0 but also gives the two earlier eras of health care a stinging rebuke.

Behind us lies a long-lost, nostalgia-tinged world of unfettered physician autonomy, sacred doctor-patient relationships, and a laser-like focus on the art and humanity of medicine. This was the world of my father, an immigrant and primary care physician in rural California. The world of Health care 1.0. While many still pine for these "good old days" of medicine, we shouldn't forget that those days weren't really all that good. With unfettered autonomy came high costs and spotty quality. Evidence-based medicine didn't exist; it was consensus and intuition. Volume-based fee-for-service payments incentivized doing things to people, instead of for people. And although the relationship was sacred, the doctor often played the role of captain of the ship, with the rest of the health care team and the patients subordinate.

So, in response to these shortcomings we now have Health care 2.0. The era of Big Medicine. Large corporate groups buying practices and hospitals, managed care and Obamacare, randomized controlled trials and evidence-based guidelines, EMRs, PQRS, HCAHPS, MACRA, Press Ganey, Lean, Six-Sigma. It is the era of Medicine As Machine...of Medicine As Assembly Line. And we—clinicians and patients—are the cogs in the machinery. Instead of ceding authority to physicians, we cede authority to government, administrators, and faceless algorithms. We more often treat a computer screen than a patient. And the doc isn't the boss, but neither is the rest of the health care team—nor the patient. We are ALL treated as commodities...raw materials in the factory.

Health 3.0 Vision

Dr. Damania goes on to describe Health 3.0 as follows:

Taking the best aspects of 1.0 (deep sacred relationships, physician autonomy) and the key pieces of 2.0 (technology, evidence, teams, systems thinking), Health 3.0 restores the human relationship at the heart of healing while bolstering it with a team that revolves around the patient while supporting each other as fellow caregivers. What emerges is vastly greater than the sum of the parts.

Caregivers and patients have the time and space and support to develop deep relationships. Providers hold patients accountable for their health, while empowered patients hold us accountable to be their guides and to know them—and treat them—as unique human beings. Our EHRs bind us and support us, rather than obstruct us. The promise of Big Data is translated to the unique patient in front of us. Our team provides the lift so everything doesn't fall on one set of shoulders anymore (health coaches, nurses, social workers, lab techs, EVERYONE together). We are evidence-empowered but not evidence-enslaved. We are paid to keep people healthy, not to click boxes while trying to chase an ever-shrinking piece of the health care pie. Our administrators seek to grow the entire pie instead, for the benefit of ALL stakeholders.

As I've shared this framework, I've received a couple of questions/comments to the effect of "where's insurance?" It's not here as it's not about who is assuming the financial risk. That varies by country and, even in the U.S., most risk is assumed by employers or various government entities at the state and federal level. The "insurance" companies are largely claims processors (typically only about one-third of the claims insurance companies process are their funds at risk). No matter who carries the risk, we're bad at purchasing health care and health & wellness services in the U.S. This framework suggests we need to take a fresh look, rather than buying what has been radically underperforming.

The pyramid graphic below is the start of developing a North Star for how various elements of health and health care interrelate with each other. It's going to require some verbal explanation of where we're going with this. The "we" is Dr. Venu Julapalli, Dr. Zubin Damania (aka ZDoggMD), Jonathan Bush, and Dr. Vinay Julapalli. The problem we're trying to address is how health care is "organized" in a tangled jumble of silos largely organized around medical technologies, not individuals (patients). It's exacerbated by economic models and information technology that further impair healing. We believe that fostering an ecosystem that is antifragile should be one of the key design points.[154] Flawed thinking looks at health care simply as an expense (or, from the perspective of the health care industry, revenue to be maximized). As Churchill states, when health is looked at as an asset, it causes one to optimize for something completely different.

For those unfamiliar with Nassim Taleb's book, *Antifragile*, he introduces the book as follows:

> Some things benefit from shocks; they thrive and grow when exposed to volatility, randomness, disorder, and stressors and love adventure, risk, and uncertainty. Yet, in spite of the ubiquity of the phenomenon, there is no word for the exact opposite of fragile. Let us call it antifragile. Antifragility is beyond resilience or robustness. The resilient resists shocks and stays the same; the antifragile gets better.

Health care has been unique in that it uses technology as an excuse for costs to go up and productivity to go down. In Health 3.0, a properly organized health ecosystem can benefit from technology rather than helping fuel hyperinflation for all of us, while decreasing productivity and job satisfaction for clinicians.

Figure 14 is a thumbnail sketch for how the pyramid works. You can also explore an interactive graphic at healthrosetta.org/health30. Each layer represents a level of care or self-care. You want to spend as much of your life as possible in self-care at the bottom of the pyramid.* When you have to move to higher layers, you want to move back down asap.

Each pyramid layer has four facets, one for each side of the pyramid.

1. Optimal way to deliver health services
2. Optimal way to pay for care
3. Enabling technology for #1 & #2
4. Enabling government role for #1 & #2

Following a given layer (e.g., value-based primary care 3.0) shows how the four facets apply to that layer.

Note that self-care is necessary at all levels. However, it starts at the foundation. The pyramid is a holarchy. This just means it incorporates hierarchies that both transcend and include levels. They work like 3D concentric circles, rather than rungs on a ladder. Imagine looking at the pyramid from the top. You will have concentric boxes, with self-care transcending and including them all.

Figure 15.

You read the pyramid from the bottom and at each layer look at the four facets to ensure they are meeting your goals. Thus, you would see that the self-care layer is at the bottom. When you access the health care system next generation primary care is where you should start. In places like Denmark and the best value-based primary care organizations in the U.S., over 90 percent of care can be addressed in a proper primary care setting. Full valued-based primary care includes things like behavioral health, interior work, health coaches, and physical therapy, all enabled by technology like secure messaging, remote monitoring, and other future advances.

Chapter 14 covers value-based primary care and focuses on high-cost individuals who consume the vast majority of health care spending. For the majority of people who have simpler primary care needs, there are more streamlined, technology-enabled, and cost-effective methods of delivery. For example, Dr. Jay Parkinson has proposed what he calls "Primary Care 3.0" which is optimized for the majority of people with simple medical needs.[155]

If an issue can't be addressed in primary care, you move up to the diagnostic layer (e.g., lab tests) for deeper insight to rule in/out various issues. Then, if you need a prescription, you'd go to the next layer—pharmacy woven into primary care. Organizations such as ChenMed do this well. If a prescription isn't the answer, you proceed to the next layer for a "professional consultation". This is a consult between the PCP and an unconflicted specialist. In this context, unconflicted means that the specialist wouldn't be performing an intervention or procedure, thus removing the profit incentive to overtreat. If an intervention is needed, you proceed to the next layer—intervention via focused care setting with deep experience in the intervention.

Jonathan Bush, CEO of athenahealth, told me about his own knee surgery and finding that even the highest-volume knee surgeons in Boston only do less than one-third of what they could. They spend the rest of their time doing a bunch marketing they'd rather not do (e.g., be a "team doctor" for a sports team to market themselves). Most would rather spend the majority of their time doing what they do best. If they did, they could drop their unit price.

Finally, for the unfortunate few who have rare and highly complex conditions, they'd go to a Center of Excellence (CoE) in their condition like the NIH, Mayo, etc. at the top of the pyramid.

To reiterate, even when at higher levels of the pyramid, the goal is to move back down the pyramid as soon as possible.

As I developed this framework further, I was interested in getting specialists' feedback. Relatively speaking, I've spent more time with primary care physicians at the base of the pyramid. The most advanced and successful value-based primary care organizations intuitively understand two key issues that drive costs and quality.

1. Fostering self-care and caregiving by nonprofessional loved ones is essential to optimizing healing and health.

2. Without a seasoned "ship captain" (the primary care physician), rough medical seas cause patients to needlessly suffer from an uncoordinated health care system.

Specialists, like any group of humans, have many opinions, but I will share the feedback from Dr. Venu Julapalli on the framework (he has also been writing about the tenets of Health 3.0).[156] The following are Dr. Julapalli's comments, edited for length and clarity.

I am loving what you guys have come up with.

1. *It starts with self-care at the base. That's key. It underscores personal responsibility in health, which has been woefully neglected. At the same time, social determinants of health (SDoH) are right at the base, where they belong. I love the pyramid's government facet, letting it act as the market accelerator, not an overly active market participant without the ability to enable the most effective and efficient system.*
2. *It properly puts value-based primary care right near the base. As a specialist, I don't need to be near the base. I also need to have as few conflicts of interest as possible in my interactions with primary care.*
3. *It properly puts the specialist care in focused settings near the top (this position doesn't make them the most important, just the most focused). This is what Devi Shetty is executing in India and Cayman Islands—high-volume cardiovascular surgery by experts who love what they do, while dropping unit price ridiculously through streamlined operations and economies of scale.[157]*
4. *It appropriately puts Centers of Excellence at the very top—go there for help with rare diagnoses, but keep it limited. We should also never forget the power of the engaged patient, who destroys the most expert doctors when love for life takes over. See this article as an example, "His Doctors Were Stumped. Then He Took Over."[158]*

Overall, I love this pyramid framework. Conceptually, it's honoring much of what I've come to believe on health care, health, and healing. You're distilling what real-life experiences and data have shown works in health care.

I will conclude with a quote highlighting how we need a major overhaul. Simply shifting who pays is just moving deck chairs on the Titanic. Metaphorically, we're all on the same ship. Dr. Otis Brawley, chief medical officer for the American Cancer Society said, "I have seen enough to conclude that no incident of failure in American medicine should be dismissed as an aberration. Failure is the system."

APPENDIX F

HEALTH 3.0 VISION

IMPLICATIONS FOR PROVIDERS, GOVERNMENT, AND STARTUPS

In the Health 3.0 Vision appendix, we laid out the failings of Health care 1.0 and 2.0 that have primed us for Health 3.0. Despite these failings, we should keep the positive and necessary elements. It's hard to argue that it's not an especially challenging time for nearly anyone in health care. We have epidemic levels of burnout amongst doctors,[159] only 20 percent of physicians report being engaged,[160] health care organizations are struggling to keep up with every-changing reimbursement and quality rules, and well-intentioned government initiatives continue to inadvertently slow rapid-pace innovation. Without a common vision and framework of what Health 3.0 should look like, we'll remain where we are, failing to activate the full potential from our collective passion, resources, and efforts. Even eight Olympic-caliber rowers can't make headway without a common goal and view of the course ahead.

In Health 3.0, the fragmented, uncoordinated health care jumble we know today must be replaced with a unified interplay of these four key elements.

1. Health & wellness services
2. Health & wellness services purchasing practices
3. Technology embedded throughout health care
4. The role of government

Health care is frequently a jumble of uncoordinated silos organized around medical technology, rather than people. This has led to a suboptimal experience for both patients and clinicians. This is often made worse by incentives that run counter to optimizing health outcomes.

The Health 3.0 framework has high-level implications for the following key audiences.

Health Care Provider Organizations

Major trends are making the care delivery elements of Health 3.0 a once-in-a-career opportunity (or threat). Just in the U.S. experts expect $1 trillion of annual revenue to shift from one set of health care players to another over the next decade.[161] This is a byproduct of the transition to purchasing health care with accountability baked in. Here are three ways health care provider organizations can advance and thrive in a Health 3.0 world.

1. Sell health services conveniently & be accountable for the value you deliver

Various new primary care models such as onsite/near-site clinics and direct primary care have significantly expanded their scope of services (remote monitoring, health coaching, etc.). The top performers readily put their fees at risk (e.g., Vera Whole Health, Privia, Iora Health, etc.). Medicare Advantage programs are taking off like wildfire, with the top performers delivering care far differently than in volume-driven models. If you're a health care provider, this is the future!

We expect Medicare Advantage to continue to grow and Medicaid Advantage to follow closely behind. This can't be dismissed as fringe when two early adopter organizations (Care-

More and HealthCare Partners) were acquired for over $5 billion and there has been over $1.2 billion invested in next generation primary care models in the past couple of years.[162] Sadly, we hear of too many organizations trying to foolishly cling to fee-for ser- vice and even enacting anti-competitive practices such as threat- ening doctors in their communities who don't refer to them (e.g., blocking data and patient flows).[163] Our message to you, is don't be scared, be brave. Be among the early organizations that figure out and master how to thrive in the inevitable future.

2. Millennials, they're a comin'

If you thought boomers were a big deal, millennials dwarf them and are transforming markets. This has already had a devastating impact on a local oligopolistic market (newspa- pers) similar to health care.[164] In another area of health, Big Food and Big Soda have had their worst earnings in decades caused by millennials having significantly different purchasing habits than their parents. The status quo in our current legacy health care system is nearly a perfect opposite of what millenni- als want and value. Organizations that think they're entitled to their patients' kids are in for a rude awakening. For most pro- vider organizations, private employers are their most lucrative revenue stream. Millennials are already the biggest chunk of the workforce and expected to be 75 percent of the workforce in 10 years. As millennials wake up to the reality that they will be indentured servants to the health care system without change, expect their voices to be heard like never before. Health 3.0 is just what millennials want.

3. Destructive doctor relationships will destroy hospi- tals' success

It's not just doctors that feel abused by the Health care 2.0 system. However, the economic impact of doctors leaving in droves to new players and from burnout will enormously harm health systems. The ZDoggMD "Lose Yourself" anthem highlights the rising revolution of nurses, doctors and clinicians who are saying "enough" and leaving for organizations focused on the Quadruple Aim.[165]

Government Officials

With Health 3.0, government will experience implications within the many roles it plays.

1. Be a smart buyer

It seems every local, state, and federal government entity is struggling with budget challenges—largely the result of health benefits being the second biggest expense after wages for many entities. As one public entity found, the best way to slash health care costs is to improve benefits (e.g., greatly improved access to value-based primary care).[166] Innovative new health care delivery organizations can serve a broader audience faster if the government is an early adopter of higher-performing health benefits. The employee and government entity can both win when employees get access to superior care that also reduces total health spending. Money is freed up to contribute to the other social determinants of health that governments can impact.

2. Don't rob from Peter to pay Paul

Government is in a unique position to improve public health and other social determinants of health. Sadly, hyper-inflating health benefits costs unnecessarily steal funds from public health and social determinant programs. These social and economic factors drive ~40 percent of health outcomes, while clinical care only drives ~20 percent.[167] Yet it consumes far more financial resources. Wise government leaders recognize the opportunity for cultivating what we call economic development 3.0, playing the high-performance health care system card. Those that have done this have created enormous value for their constituents.[168] We all intuitively know that health care spending comes at the expense of other household spending. Economic Development 3.0 properly aligns limited public resources to improve social determinants of health and reduce middle class wage stagnation.[169]

3. Why accept in health care what we'd never accept elsewhere?

Imagine if local, state, and federal government contracts for road and highway construction did not require smooth connections between road sections. This is exactly what happens in health care. We pay trillions of taxpayer dollars to tax-exempt health care organizations (many health systems are tax-exempt), yet permit them to prevent implementation of many simple care improving processes, reporting, and technologies, such as simple exchange of vital patient information critical to enabling clinicians to provide high-quality care. Collectively, trillions have gone to health care organizations that lack even basic modern connectivity. Nowhere in our society are more lives in jeopardy. It's like military generals who are actively prevented from seeing the full battlefield.

Even worse from a public health perspective is the status quo's limited ability to facilitate two-way communication in crisis situations. We've seen this recently with Zika. Modern, clouded-based electronic health record and other communication systems can rapidly identify and respond to public health threats, identifying regions and individuals at greatest risk.[170] Yet most organizations use outdated systems that require manual updates. This unnecessarily imperils the most vulnerable in society.

4. Get out of the way!

Sadly, many well-intentioned government efforts have damaging unintended consequences. Government officials should adopt a Hippocratic Oath of sorts. Too often, recognizing the damage caused by policy mistakes and the subsequent confessions come too late.[171] Government should avoid defining technology innovation and what connectedness looks like, instead focusing on rewarding adopting it. Stop dictating how technology companies share data and information. Demand that the private sector deliver the right outcomes—information flowing from all clinical data sources—then let the private sector complete that work.

Technology Startups

Innovate with the Like-Minded—Where's that Puck Going?

Avoid the hazard of selling to large health care organizations too early, which is often terrible advice investors and others give (e.g., land a big account)Innovation takes time to incubate in smaller organizations before expanding to larger organizations. Typically, traditional large health care organizations aren't far enough ahead of the curve on Health 3.0 to be the most valuable early customers.

Further, there are entirely new digital health opportunities that span beyond traditional health care systems. In the population health era, a true population health manager could be a city health commissioner that looks beyond the sick care system. Don't focus on where the world is, think where health-related services might and should go. That is likely more fertile ground for a startup in their early years. A good rule of thumb is don't pursue a provider that is bigger than your current install base.

Health 3.0 is an exciting world where hospital CEOs aren't in the conflicted position of being rewarded to fill beds like a hotel manager. It puts health in the community. Health systems should rejoice that their new financial incentives are aligned with their missions, unlike the status quo that incentivizes the opposite.

The great news is that many hospital CEOs are just as excited about Health 3.0 as the hundreds of thousands of clinicians activating to drive towards a health ecosystem that works for everyone.

AUTHOR BIO

Dave Chase conceived of the Health Rosetta. Its application has two main pillars.

1. **Impact** – Chase is a cofounder of the Health Rosetta Ecosystem. This includes an education/certification entity that is a LEED-like organization for health care. It advances the Health Rosetta blueprint for purchasing health care wisely. The ecosystem's primary initial focus is on the U.S. employer health care market, although the Health Rosetta isn't inherently employer or U.S. specific.
2. **Investment and company building** – Chase is a cofounder of the Health Rosetta Group, a holding company and investment group that backs the transformation of health care. It includes the Quad Aim Fund, a seed stage venture fund, and an innovative acquisition and transformation model for building next-gen services companies.

Chase's TEDx talk entitled "Health Care Stole the American Dream - Here's How We Take It Back" sums up health care's devastation of the middle class and the redemption coming via a grassroots movement. It can be viewed at healthrosetta.org/tedx. Chase was named one of the most influential people in Digital Health because of his entrepreneurial success, speaking, and writing. He delights in sharing how high-performing organizations have solved health care's toughest challenges. Chase coauthored the 2014 health care Book of the Year awarded by HIMSS entitled *Engage! Transforming Healthcare Through Digital Patient Engagement.*

Chase was the CEO and Cofounder of Avado, acquired by & integrated into WebMD & Medscape (the most widely used health care professional site). Before Avado, Chase spent several years outside of health care in startups as a founder or in consulting roles with LiveRez.com, MarketLeader, and WhatCounts. He was also on the founding & leadership teams in two $1B+ businesses within Microsoft including their $2 billion health care platform business.

Chase is a father of two great kids/athletes, husband, and oxygen-fueled mountain athlete. His team placed 3rd in their division and 24th overall (of 500 teams) in the oldest adventure race in the U.S. where Dave tackled the Nordic ski leg. Dave is also a former PAC-12 800 Meter competitor.

BIBLIOGRAPHY & ENDNOTES

[1] Joe Eaton and M.B. Pell, "Lobbyists Swarm Capitol to Influence Health Reform," *The Center for Public Integrity* (May 19, 2014), accessed July 4, 2016 https://www.publicintegrity.org/2010/02/24/2725/lobbyists-swarm-capitol-influence-health-reform.

[2] Arnold S. Relman, M.D., "The New Medical-Industrial Complex," *The New England Journal of Medicine* (1980): 303, accessed July 4, 2016, DOI: 10.1056/NEJM198010233031703

[3] David I Auerbach and Arthur L. Kellermann, *How Does Growth in Health Care Costs Affect the American Family?* (Santa Monica, CA: RAND Corporation, 2011), https://www.rand.org/pubs/research_briefs/RB9605.html.

[4] "The Big Picture: The Burden of Musculoskeletal Disease in the United States," United States Bone and Joint Initiative, accessed July 4, 2016, http://www.boneandjointburden.org/2014-report/i0/big-picture

[5] Organization for Economic Cooperation and Development, OECD Health Data 2011 (Nov, 2011).

[6] Kim Chul M.D., M.P.H. and Vinay Prasad, M.D., M.P.H., "Cancer Drugs Approved on the Basis of a Surrogate End Point and Subsequent Overall Survival: An Analysis of 5 Years of US Food and Drug Administration Approvals," *JAMA Intern Med.* 175 (2010): 12, accessed July 4, 2016, doi:10.1001/jamainternmed.2015.5868

[7] A.L. Kellermann and D.I. Auerbach, *The Rand Blog,* (January, 3, 2013), http://www.rand.org/blog/2013/01/health-care-cost-growth-is-hurting-middle-class-families.html.

[8] "Health Care Costs: A Primer," The Henry J. Kaiser Family Foundation, accessed July 4, 2016, http://www.kff.org/report-section/health-care-costs-a-primer-2012-report/

[9] Anna Louie Sussman, "Burden of Health-Care Costs Moves to the Middle Class," *The Wall Street Journal*, access December 12, 2016, https://www.wsj.com/articles/burden-of-health-care-costs-moves-to-the-middle-class-1472166246

[10] "US Health Care Spending: Who Pays?," California Health Care Foundation, accessed July 4, 2016, http://www.chcf.org/publications/2015/12/data-viz-hcc-national

[11] Angela Mueller, "Supreme Court rules for Schlichter Client in 401(k) case," *St. Louis Business Journal*, accessed July 4, 2016, http://www.bizjournals.com/stlouis/news/2015/05/18/supreme-court-rules-for-schlichter-client-in-401-k.html

[12] The core issue is that ERISA health plan dollars are viewed under case law as the employer's, not the employee's. However, the Department of Labor even says these fiduciary duties apply on their website. "Health Plans & Benefits: Fiduciary Responsibilities," United States Department of Labor, accessed January 10, 2017, https://www.dol.gov/general/topic/health-plans/fiduciaryresp. In fairness to the DoL, prior to high-deductible plans it was once easier to argue that health benefits spending was the "employer's money." But today 51 percent of the workforce has a deductible of more than $1,000. "Section Eight: High-Deductible Health Plans with Savings Option," The Henry J. Kaiser Family Foundation, accessed December 5, 2016, http://www.kff.org/report-section/ehbs-2016-section-eight-high-deductible-health-plans-with-savings-option/. With cost-sharing and high-deductibles, employees are typically paying approximately 30 percent of health benefits costs. "2016 Employer Health Benefits Survey," The Henry J. Kaiser Family Foundation, accessed December 5, 2016, http://www.kff.org/health-costs/report/2016-employer-health-benefits-survey/

[13] David I. Auerbach and Arthur L. Kellermann, "How Does Growth in Health Care Costs Affect the American Family?" accessed July 4, 2016, https://www.rand.org/pubs/research_briefs/RB9605.html

[14] Modupe Idowu, "Premium Hikes Eat Up Teacher Pay Raise," accessed October 14, 2016, http://local15tv.com/news/local/premium-hikes-eat-up-teacher-pay-raise

[15] "Make America Make Again: Manufacturing in the U.S.A.," WAMU/NPR., accessed February 1, 2017, http://the1a.org/shows/2017-01-25/made-in-america

[16] Barry Ritholtz, "Health-Care Costs Ate Your Pay Raises," accessed November 5, 2016, https://www.bloomberg.com/view/articles/2016-09-28/health-care-costs-ate-your-pay-raises

[17] Richard A. Young, M.D., "Who Will Have Health Insurance in the Future? An Updated Projection," *Annals Family Medicine* 10 (2010): 2 accessed July 4, 2016, doi: 10.13americans with less than 1,000 in sss70/afm.1348

[18] Cameron Huddleston, "69% of Americans Have Less Than $1,000 in Savings," accessed November 4, 2016, https://www.gobankingrates.com/personal-finance/data-americans-savings/.

[19] David U. Himmelstein, M.D. et al., "Medical Bankruptcy in the United States, 2007: Results of a National Study," accessed July 4, 2016 http://www.pnhp.org/new_bankruptcy_study/Bankruptcy-2009.pdf

[20] Christina Lamontagne, "NerdWallet Health finds Medical Bankruptcy accounts for majority of personal bankruptcies," accessed July 4, 2016, https://www.nerdwallet.com/blog/health/managing-medical-bills/nerdwallet-health-study-estimates-56-million-americans-65-struggle-medical-bills-2013-2/

[21] "American Health Care Tragedies Are Taking Over Crowdfunding," accessed July 4, 2017 https://www.bloomberg.com/news/articles/2017-06-12/america-s-health-care-crisis-is-a-gold-mine-for-crowdfunding

[22] Health Policy Commission, "List of Figures in 2013 Cost Trends Report by the Health Policy Commission," accessed July 4 2016, http://www.mass.gov/anf/docs/hpc/2013-ctr-chartbook.pdf

[23] Susan Brink, "How Health Care Costs Affect Small Town Living," accessed July 4, 2016, http://health.usnews.com/health-news/hospital-of-tomorrow/articles/2014/02/05/how-health-care-costs-affect-small-town-living

[24] JJohn T. James, "A New, Evidence-based Estimate of Patient Harms Associated with Hospital Care" *Journal of Patient Safety* 9 (2013): 3, accessed July 4, 2016, doi:10.1097/PTS.0b013e3182948a69;" Medical Errors Are No. 3 Cause Of U.S Deaths, Researchers Say," *NPR: Boise State Public Radio*, accessed July 4, 2016, http://www.npr.org/sections/health-shots/2016/05/03/476636183/death-certificates-undercount-toll-of-medical-errors; "Study Suggests Medical Errors Now Third Leading Cause of Death in the U.S.," *John Hopkins Medicine*, accessed July 4, 2017, http://www.hopkinsmedicine.org/news/media/releases/study_suggests_medical_errors_now_third_leading_cause_of_death_in_the_us

[25] Ariana Eunjung Cha, "Researchers: Medical Errors Now Third Leading Cause of Death in United States," The Washington Post, May 3, 2016, accessed July 4, 2016, https://www.washingtonpost.com/news/to-your-health/wp/2016/05/03/researchers-medical-errors-now-third-leading-cause-of-death-in-united-states/?utm_term=.0c773eff4155

[26] Jon Krakauer, *Where Men Win Glory: The Odyssey of Pat Tillman*. (New York: Doubleday, 2010), 343; "United States Military Casualties of War," Wikipedia, accessed July 4, 2017, https://en.wikipedia.org/wiki/United_States_military_casualties_of_warr

[27] Sarah Kliff, "Do no harm," *Vox*, accessed July 4, 2016, http://www.vox.com/2015/7/9/8905959/medical-harm-infection-prevention

[28] Marty Makary, *Unaccountable: What Hospitals Won't Tell You and How Transparency Can Revolutionize Health Care*. (London: Bloomsbury, 2012)

[29] For this calculation, I compared actual health care premium growth rates with historical rates of inflation, then assumed the difference would have been invested in an S&P index fund and that dividends would have been reinvested.

[30] The Pew Charitable Trusts, "Retirement Plan Access and Participation Across Generations," accessed March 2, 2017, http://www.pewtrusts.org/en/research-and-analysis/issue-briefs/2017/02/retirement-plan-access-and-participation-across-generations; Sean Williams, "Nearly 7 in 10 Americans Have Less Than $1,000 in Savings," *USA Today*, accessed March 2, 2017, https://www.usatoday.com/story/money/personalfinance/2016/10/09/savings-study/91083712/

[31] Samer W. Cabbabe, M.D., "The Medical Profession Has a Bad Reputation. Here's Why," Kevin MD, March 1, 2017, http://www.kevinmd.com/blog/2017/03/medical-profession-bad-reputation-heres.html

[32] Christine Sinsky, M.D. et al., "Allocation of Physician Time in Ambulatory Practice: A Time and Motion Study in 4 Specialties," *Annals of Internal Medicine* 165 (2016): 11, accessed January 4, 2016, DOI: 10.7326/M16-0961

[33] Sandra G. Boodman, "Patients Lose When Doctors Can't Do Good Physical Exams," *Kaiser Health News*, accessed July 4, 2016, http://khn.org/news/patients-lose-when-doctors-do-not-perform-physical-exams-correctly/

[34] Christine Sinsky, M.D. et al., "Allocation of Physician Time in Ambulatory Practice: A Time and Motion Study in 4 Specialties."

[35] Ken Murray, M.D., "How Doctors Die" *Saturday Evening Post* March/April 2013, accessed July 4, 2016, http://www.saturdayeveningpost.com/2013/03/06/in-the-magazine/health-in-the-magazine/how-doctors-die.html

[36] Craig Hatkoff, Rabbi Irwin Kula, and Zach Levine, "How to Die in America: Welcome to La Crosse, Wisconsin" *Forbes* (September 23, 2014), accessed July 4, 2016, https://www.forbes.com/sites/offwhitepapers/2014/09/23/how-to-die-in-america-welcome-to-la-crosse/#17df59bbe8c6

[37] David Epstein & Propublica, "When Evidence Says No, but Doctors Say Yes," *The Atlantic*. (February 22, 2017), https://www.theatlantic.com/health/archive/2017/02/when-evidence-says-no-but-doctors-say-yes/517368/

[38] Gina Kolata, "Why 'Useless' Surgery Is Still Popular," *The New York Times* (August 3, 2016), accessed July 4, 2016, https://www.nytimes.com/2016/08/04/upshot/the-right-to-know-that-an-operation-is-next-to-useless.html

[39] "Infographic: Health Care Waste," *PBS News Hour* (July 4, 20126), http://www.pbs.org/newshour/multimedia/health-750b/

[40] This chart is adapted from one provided to me by an industry insider.

[41] "How Many Doctors Does It Take to Start a Healthcare Revolution? Full Transcript," *Freakonomics* (April 9, 2015), http://freakonomics.com/2015/04/09/how-many-doctors-does-it-take-to-start-a-healthcare-revolution-full-transcript/

[42] Atul Gawande," The Hot Spotters," *The New Yorker* (January 24, 2011), accessed July 4 2016, http://www.newyorker.com/magazine/2011/01/24/the-hot-spotters

[43] This data comes from ClearHealthCosts internal datasets that they've given us permission to use.

[44] "2016 Employer Health Benefits Survey," The Henry J. Kaiser Family Foundation.

[45] This data comes from ClearHealthCosts internal datasets that they've given us permission to use.

[46] Private discussions with other industry executives and experts not for attribution.

[47] "FRAUD, WASTE AND ABUSE IN SOCIAL SERVICES: Identifying and Overcoming this Modern-Day Epidemic," Accenture Consulting, accessed March 2, 2017, https://www.accenture.com/us-en/insight-fraud-waste-abuse-social-services-summary

[48] Private discussions with other industry executives and experts not for attribution.

[49] "HRI Benefits Advisor Compensation Disclosure Form," Health Rosetta, accessed May 25, 2017, https://healthrosetta.org/learn/benefits-advisor-disclosure/

[50] Richard Fry, "Millennials Surpass Gen Xers as the Largest Generation in U.S. Labor Force," Pew Research Center, (July 4th, 2016), http://www.pewre-

search.org/fact-tank/2015/05/11/millennials-surpass-gen-x ers-as-the-larg-est-generation-in-u-s-labor-force/

[51] David Goldhill, *Catastrophic Care: Why Everything We Think We Know about Health Care Is Wrong* (New York: Knopf Doubleday Publishing Group, 2013)

[52] Ibid., 59.

[53] Cascadia Capital, "The Future Health Ecosystem Today" (January 15, 2016). Datapoints from Robert Wood Johnson Foundation, https://www.forbes.com/sites/davechase/2016/02/03/report-the-future-health-ecosystem-to-day-provides-look-into-healthcares-future/#1f9cc7065171

[54] Danny Crichton, "Millennials Are Destroying Banks, and It's the Banks' Fault," *TechCrunch* (May 30, 2015), https://techcrunch.com/2015/05/30/millennial-banks/

[55] Adam Hanft,"The Stunning Evolution of Millennials: They've Become the Ben Franklin Generation," *THE BLOG Huffington Post* (August 11, 2015), http://www.huffingtonpost.com/adam-hanft/the-stunning-evolu-tion-of_b_6108412.html

[56] Danny Crichton, "Millennials Are Destroying Banks, and It's the Banks' Fault."

[57] Christina Farr, "Are Millennials Ready to Ditch their Regular Doctor?" *KQED Science Future of You,* (August 12, 2015), http://ww2.kqed.org/futu-reofyou/2015/08/12/convenience-or-loyalty-what-do-millennials-value-more-when-it-comes-to-their-health

[58] Robert Wood Johnson Foundation, "Growing Retail Clinic Industry Employs, Empowers Nurse Practitioners," accessed July 4, 2016, http://www.rwjf.org/en/library/articles-and-news/2015/02/growing-retail-clin-ic-industry-employs--empowers-nurse-practitio.html; Craig E Pollack et al., "The Growth Of Retail Clinics And The Medical Home: Two Trends In Con-cert Or In Conflict?," *Health Affairs* (29); 5, accessed July 4 2016, doi: 10.1377/hlthaff.2010.0089; Bruce Jaspen, "Retail Clinics Hit 10 Million Annual Visits But Just 2% Of Primary Care Market," Forbes, accessed July 4, 2016, https://www.forbes.com/sites/brucejapsen/2015/04/23/retail-clinics-hit-10-mil-lion-annual-visits-but-just-2-of-primary-care-market

[59] Jason Hidalgo, "Here's How Millennials Could Change Health Care" *USA Today* (February 7, 2016), http://www.usatoday.com/story/news/poli-tics/elections/2016/02/07/heres-how-millennials-could-change-health-care/79818756/

[60] "People Love Their Health Benefits. But Do They Understand Them?" Collective Health (2016), https://collectivehealth.com/insights/consumer-health-benefits-survey-2015/

[61] Ibid.

[62] Fred Dews, "Brookings Data Now: 75 Percent of 2025 Workforce Will Be Millennials," accessed July 4, 2016, https://www.brookings.edu/blog/brookings-now/2014/07/17/brookings-data-now-75-percent-of-2025-workforce-will-be-millennials/; Alastair Mitchell, "The Rise of the Millennial Workforce," *Wired*, accessed May 25, 2017, https://www.wired.com/insights/2013/08/the-rise-of-the-millennial-workforce/

[63] "The Price of Excess* Identifying Waste in Healthcare Spending," PricewaterhouseCoopers' Health Research Institute, accessed January 22, 2017, http://www.oss.net/dynamaster/file_archive/080509/59f26a38c114f2295757bb-6be522128a/The%20Price%20of%20Excess%20-%20Identifying%20Waste%20in%20Healthcare%20Spending%20-%20PWC.pdf

[64] "US Health Care Spending: Who Pays?" California Health Care Foundation.

[65] Robert Kocher, M.D., and Nikhil R. Sahni, B.S., "Rethinking Health Care Labor" *The New England Journal of Medicine* (2011): 365, accessed July 4, 2016, DOI: 10.1056/NEJMp1109649

[66] Ibid.

[67] David Dayen, "The Hidden Monopolies That Raise Drug Prices," *The American Prospect Longform*, accessed May 17, 2017, http://prospect.org/article/hidden-monopolies-raise-drug-prices; Thomas A. Hemphill, "THE "TROUBLES" WITH PHARMACY BENEFIT MANAGERS," CATO Institute, accessed June 1, 2017, https://object.cato.org/sites/cato.org/files/serials/files/regulation/2017/3/regulation-v40n1-5.pdf

[68] Tim Thomas, "Your PBM Adds Drugs Like Duexis to Your Formulary; Why Should You Have to Pay?" Crystal Clear Rx, accessed March 2, 2017, http://crystalclearrx.com/your-pbm-adds-drugs-duexis-your-formulary-why-should-you-have-pay

[69] Mark Flores, "United HealthCare Administered ERISA Plan Sued for Embezzlement in Medical Claims Overpayment Offset Dispute," AVYM, accessed July 4, 2016, http://avym.com/united-healthcare-administered-erisa-plan-sued-for-embezzlement-in-medical-claims-overpayment-offset-dispute/

[70] Tara Parker-Pope "How Doctors and Patients Do Harm" *New York Times Well* (April 20, 2012), https://well.blogs.nytimes.com/2012/04/20/how-doctors-and-patients-do-harm/

[71] Jamie Ducharme, "Misdiagnosing Cancer is More Common Than We Think" *Boston Wellness* (January 31, 2013), http://www.bostonmagazine.com/health/blog/2013/01/31/study-cancer-misdiagnose/

[72] Dr. Alan Greene, "Jumping out of a Plane More Than 47 Times Safer Than Checking into a Hospital. Unless…" *Dr. Greene's Blog* (July 27, 2011), https://www.drgreene.com/jumping-plane-47-times-safer-checking-hospital/

[73] "Top Industries," OpenSecrets.org, accessed, July 4, 2017, https://www.opensecrets.org/lobby/top.php?indexType=i

[74] "Leapfrog Hospital Safety Grade," http://www.hospitalsafetygrade.org/

[75] "Hospital Compare," *Medicare.gov*, accessed July 4 2016, https://www.medicare.gov/hospitalcompare

[76] "HR Consulting in the US: Market Research Report," *IBISWorld*, accessed June 3, 2017, https://www.ibisworld.com/industry-trends/market-research-reports/professional-scientific-technical-services/professional-scientific-technical-services/hr-consulting.html

[77] Michael Dendy, "The OPEC of Healthcare," *LinkedIn*, accessed July 4, 2016, https://www.linkedin.com/pulse/opec-healthcare-michael-mike-dendy

[78] Rod Dunlap, "Robotic Process Automation: A Better Way to Boost Auto-Adjudication Rates," *hfma*, accessed July 4, 2016, https://www.hfma.org/Content.aspx?id=48424 . The number cited here is 80%, but multiple industry insiders have told me it's more like 90+% in private conversations.

[79] Private discussions with other industry executives and experts not for attribution.

[80] "FRAUD, WASTE AND ABUSE IN SOCIAL SERVICES: Identifying and Overcoming this Modern-Day Epidemic," Accenture Consulting.

[81] Noah Rayman, "The World's Top 5 Cybercrime Hotspots," *Time* (August 7, 2014), accessed July 4, 2016, http://time.com/3087768/the-worlds-5-cybercrime-hotspots/

[82] Fahmida Y. Rashid, "Why Hackers Want Your Health Care Data Most of All," *InfoWorld* (September 14, 2015), accessed July 4, 2016, http://www.infoworld.com/article/2983634/security/why-hackers-want-your-health-care-data-breaches-most-of-all.htmll

[83] *The Nilson Report* (October 2016): 1096, accessed January 17, 2017, https://www.nilsonreport.com/upload/content_promo/The_Nilson_Report_10-17-2016.pdf ; John S. Kiernan, "Credit Card & Debit Card Fraud Statistics," WalletHub, accessed March 2, 2017, https://wallethub.com/edu/credit-debit-card-fraud-statistics/25725/

[84] Private discussions with other industry executives and experts not for attribution.

[85] Karen Pollitz, "Workplace Wellness Programs Characteristics and Requirements," The Henry J. Kaiser Family Foundation, accessed July 4, 2016, http://www.kff.org/private-insurance/issue-brief/workplace-wellness-programs-characteristics-and-requirements/; Erika Fry, "Corporate Wellness Programs: Healthy or Hokey?" *Fortune Health* (March 15, 2017), http://fortune.com/2017/03/15/corporate-health-wellness-programs/

[86] Vince Kuraitis, "A Founding Father of DM Astonishingly Declares: 'My Kid is Ugly,'" *e-CareManagement Blog*, http://e-caremanagement.com/a-founding-father-of-dm-astonishingly-declares-my-kid-is-ugly/

[87] Michael P. O'Donnell, "My Last Lecture," *American Journal of Health Promotion* (2016): 30, accessed January 3, 2017, doi: 10.1177/0890117116671802

[88] L.V. Anderson, "Workplace Wellness Programs Are a Sham," *Slate*, accessed November 5, 2016, http://www.slate.com/articles/health_and_science/the_ladder/2016/09/workplace_wellness_programs_are_a_sham.html. Note the 13,000 shares on Facebook alone.

[89] "About the USPSTF," U.S. Preventive Services, accessed March 2, 2017, https://www.uspreventiveservicestaskforce.org/Page/Name/about-the-uspstf

[90] "Health Checkups: When you need them—and when you don't," *Choosing Wisely*, accessed July 4, 2016, http://www.choosingwisely.org/patient-resources/health-checkups/

[91] Al Lewis, "The 401W: A Wellness Program Even Al Lewis Could Love," *The Health Care Blog* (April 17, 2017), http://thehealthcareblog.com/blog/2017/04/17/the-401w-a-wellness-program-even-al-lewis-could-love/

[92] Al Lewis, "A Wellness Program Everyone Can Love," *Insurance Thought Leadership*, accessed May 17, 2017, http://insurancethoughtleadership.com/a-wellness-program-everyone-can-love/

[93] Erika Fry, "Corporate Wellness Programs: Healthy or Hokey?"

[94] Andie Burjek, "Health Literacy Empowers Employees to Make Better Decisions," *Workforce* (February 7, 2017), http://www.workforce.com/2017/02/07/health-literacy-empowers-employees-make-better-decisions/

[95] "IOM Report: Estimated $750B Wasted Annually in Health Care System," *Kaiser Health News, accessed* July 4, 2016, http://khn.org/morning-breakout/iom-report/; "The Price of Excess* Identifying Waste in Healthcare Spending," PricewaterhouseCoopers' Health Research Institute

[96] Wallace, Jean E. et al., "Physician Wellness: A Missing Quality Indicator," *The Lancet* 374: 9702, accessed July 4, 2016, http://www.thelancet.com/pdfs/journals/lancet/PIIS0140673609614240.pdf

[97] Charles Kenney, "Better, Faster, More Affordable," *Seattle Business*, accessed July 4, 2016, http://seattlebusinessmag.com//article/better-faster-more-affordable

[98] Gina Kolata, "Why 'Useless' Surgery Is Still Popular," *The New York Times*.

[99] The 67 percent number cited here is from a transparent broker based on his own experience. It's consistent with what I've encountered from many others.

[100] "Employer Health Benefits," The Kaiser Family Foundation and Health Research & Educational Trust, accessed July 4, 2016, https://kaiserfamilyfoundation.files.wordpress.com/2013/04/7936.pdf; This represents the average premium inflation rate from 2000-2009 based on the figures provided in the Kaiser/HRET 2009 Employer Health Benefits Annual Survey.

[101] Gina Kolata, "Why 'Useless' Surgery Is Still Popular," *The New York Times*.

[102] "The $272 billion swindle," The Economist, accessed July 4, 2016, https://www.economist.com/news/united-states/21603078-why-thieves-love-americas-health-care-system-272-billion-swindle

[103] "IOM Report: Estimated $750B Wasted Annually in Health Care System," Kaiser Health News

[104] "DOL Files Suit Against Macy's for Alleged Health and Welfare Plan Violations," accessed October 1, 2017, https://blogs.haynesboone.com/2017/09/20/dol-files-suit-macys-alleged-health-welfare-plan-violations/

[105] "The $272 billion swindle," The Economist

[106] Cutter, Chip. "The opioid crisis is creating a fresh hell for America's employers," accessed August 4, 2017, https://www.linkedin.com/pulse/opioid-crisis-creating-fresh-hell-americas-employers-chip-cutter/

[107] Monnat, Shannon. Deaths of Despair and Support for Trump in the 2016 Presidential Election. The Pennsylvania University Department of Agricultural Economics, Sociology, and Education Research Brief, 2016. Accessed July 4, 2017. http://aese.psu.edu/directory/smm67/Election16.pdf

[108] Alex Hollingsworth, Christopher J. Ruhm, and Kosali Simon, "Macroeconomic Conditions and Opioid Abuse," The National Bureau of Economic Research, accessed July 4, 2017, http://www.nber.org/papers/w23192

[109] "Bureau of Labor Statistics for 2016," accessed October 24, 2017, https://www.ssa.gov/cgi-bin/netcomp.cgi?year=2016

[110] Vickie Connor, "Patients With Mental Disorders Get Half Of All Opioid Prescriptions," accessed July 4, 2017, http://khn.org/news/patients-with-mental-disorders-get-half-of-all-opioid-prescriptions/

[111] Andrew Kolodny, David T. Courtwright, Catherine S. Hwang, Peter Kreiner, John L. Eadie, Thomas W. Clark, and G. Caleb Alexander, "The Prescription Opioid and Heroin Crisis: A Public Health Approach to an Epidemic of Addiction," Annual Review of Public Health 36 (2015): 559, accessed July 4, 2017, doi:10.1146/annurev-publhealth-031914-122957

[112] Thomas R. Frieden, M.D., M.P.H., and Debra Houry, M.D., M.P.H. "Reducing the Risks of Relief—The CDC Opioid-Prescribing Guideline," New England Journal of Medicine 374 (2016): 1501-1504, accessed July 4, 2017, doi: 10.1056/NEJMp1515917

[113] Roger Chou, MD; Judith A. Turner, PhD; Emily B. Devine, PharmD, PhD, MBA; Ryan N. Hansen, PharmD, PhD; Sean D. Sullivan, PhD; Ian Blazina, MPH; Tracy Dana, MLS; Christina Bougatsos, MPH; Richard A. Deyo, MD, MPH. "The Effectiveness and Risks of Long-Term Opioid Therapy for Chronic Pain: A Systematic Review for a National Institutes of Health Pathways to Prevention Workshop," Annual Internal Medicine 162 (2015): 4, accessed July 4, 2017, doi: 10.7326/M14-2559

[114] Anna Lembke, MD; Keith Humphreys, PhD; and Jordan Newmark, MD, Stanford University School of Medicine, Stanford, California "Weighing the Risks and Benefits of Chronic Opioid Therapy," American Family Physician, accessed July 4, 2017 www.aafp.org/afp/2016/0615/p982.html

[115] Kevin M. Fain, JD, MPH and G. Caleb Alexander, MD, MS. "Mind the Gap: Understanding the Effects of Pharmaceutical Direct-to-Consumer Advertising," Medical Care 52 (2014): 4, accessed July 4, 2017, doi: 10.1097/MLR.0000000000000126

[116] Rebecca Robbins. "Do Americans really watch 16 hours of pharma ads

a year?," STAT, accessed September 12, 2017, https://www.statnews.com/2017/09/12/americans-16-hours-pharma-ads/

[117] Janet K. Freburger, PT, PhD, et. al. "Rising Prevalence of Chronic Low Back Pain," Arch Intern Med. 169 (2009): 3, accessed July 4, 2017, doi: 10.1001/archinternmed.2008.543

[118] "New research reveals the trends and risk factors behind America's growing heroin epidemic" CDC, accessed July 4, 2017, https://www.cdc.gov/media/releases/2015/p0707-heroin-epidemic.html

[119] Christopher A. Viadro, "Increase in opiate usage appears tied to decrease in access to treatment in worker's compensation," ButlerViadro,LLP, accessed July 4, 2017, http://www.butlerviadro.com/blog/2016/05/increase-in-opiate-usage-appears-tied-to-decrease-in-access-to-treatment-in-workers-compensation.shtml

[120] Josh Katz, "Drug Deaths in America Are Rising Faster Than Ever," The New York Times, accessed July 4, 2017, https://www.nytimes.com/interactive/2017/06/05/upshot/opioid-epidemic-drug-overdose-deaths-are-rising-faster-than-ever.html

[121] Cutter, Chip. "The opioid crisis is creating a fresh hell for America's employers"

[122] DeWine, Mike. "Economic Aspects of Opioid Crisis" Filmed June 2017 at Longworth House Office Building, Washington D.C. Video 26:41. https://www.youtube.com/watch?v=LIQIQ1jC2dg&feature=youtu.be&t=1601

[123] Donnelly, Frank. "Staten Island Ferry ex-captain details chaos that enveloped Barberi after fatal crash," Silive.com, accessed July 4, 2017, http://www.silive.com/news/2010/07/staten_island_ferry_ex-captain.html

[124] Meier, Barry. "Pain Pills Add Cost and Delays to Job Injuries," The New York Times, accessed July 4, 2017, http://www.nytimes.com/2012/06/03/health/painkillers-add-costs-and-delays-to-workplace-injuries.html

[125] City Slashes Healthcare Costs By Improving Health Benefits Forbes February 8, 2016, accessd July 4, 2017, https://www.forbes.com/sites/davechase/2016/02/08/city-slashes-healthcare-costs-by-improving-health-benefits

[126] Joshua J. Fenton, MD, MPH, et. al."The Cost of Satisfaction: A National Study of Patient Satisfaction, Health Care Utilization, Expenditures, and Mortality" Arch Intern Med. 172 (2012): 5, accessed July 4, 2017, doi: 10.1001/archinternmed.2011.1662

[127] Jen Wieczner, "Most Millennials Think They'll Be Worse Off Than Their Par-

ents," *Fortune*, accessed August 14, 2017, http://fortune.com/2016/03/01/millennials-worse-parents-retirement/ refers to this study

[128] David Goldhill, *Catastrophic Care: Why Everything We Think We Know about Health Care Is Wrong* (New York: Knopf Doubleday Publishing Group, 2013)

[129] Dan Munro, U.S. Healthcare Actually Isn't Broken, *Insurance Thought Leadership*, accessed August 15, 2017, http://insurancethoughtleadership.com/u-s-healthcare-actually-isnt-broken/

[130] "Joanne Disch testifying on Patient Safety" C-SPAN, accessed August 15, 2017, https://www.c-span.org/video/?c4507180/joanne-disch-testifying-patient-safety-deaths; John T. James, PhD, "A New, Evidence-based Estimate of Patient Harms Associated with Hospital Care" *Journal of Patient Safety* (September 2013): 122-28, accessed August, 15 2017, http://journals.lww.com/journalpatientsafety/Fulltext/2013/09000/A_New,_Evidence_based_Estimate_of_Patient_Harms.2.aspx

[131] Al Lewis and Vik Khanna, "Corporate Wellness Programs Lose Money," accessed July 4, 2016, https://hcexchange.conference-board.org/blog/post.cfm?post=5029

[132] Ron Goetzel et al., "Workplace Programs, Policies, and Environmental Supports to Prevent Cardiovascular Disease," *Health Affairs* 36 (2017), accessed May 5, 2017, doi: 10.1377/hlthaff.2016.1273

[133] "How Much Does a Good Wellness Program Cost?" *Wellsource*, accessed July 4, 2016, https://www.wellsource.com/wp-content/uploads/2015/08/How_Much_Should_a_Wellness_Program_Cost.pdf

[134] Al Lewis, "Shattering the Wellness ROI Myth," *Insurance Thought Leadership*, accessed March 2, 2017, http://insurancethoughtleadership.com/shattering-the-wellness-roi-myth/

[135] Richard A. Hirth et al., "Connecticut's Value-Based Insurance Plan Increased the Use of Targeted Services and Medication Adherence," *Health Affairs* 35 (2016): 4, accessed July4, 2016, doi: 10.1377/hlthaff.2015.1371

[136] Arielle Levin Becker, "Study: State Employee Wellness Plan Increased Use of Preventive Care," accessed July 4, 2016, https://ctmirror.org/2016/04/05/study-state-employee-wellness-plan-increased-use-of-preventive-care/

[137] Lasse T. Krogsbøll, M.D. et al., "General Health Checks in Adults for Reducing Morbidity and Mortality from Disease," *JAMA* 309 (2013): 23, accessed July 4, 2016, doi:10.1001/jama.2013.5039

138 "Health Checkups When You Need Them—And When You Don't," *Choosing Wisely*, accessed June 1, 2017, http://www.choosingwisely.org/patient-resources/health-checkups/; Jim Lee, "Reducing "Low Value Care": Where Do We Start?" Altarum Institute, accessed July 4, 2016, http://altarum.org/health-policy-blog/reducing-"low-value-care"-where-do-we-start

139 "Program Measurement & Evaluation Guide: Core Metrics for Employee Health Management," *Population Health Alliance*, accessed July 4, 2016, http://populationhealthalliance.org/publications/program-measurement-evaluation-guide-core-metrics-for-employee-health-management.html

140 Michael O'Donnel, "Does Workplace Health Promotion Work or Not? Are You Sure You Really Want to Know the Truth?" *American Journal of Health* (2013): 28, accessed July 4, 2016, doi.org/10.4278/ajhp.28.1.iv

141 Siyan Baxter, B.N.R.N. (Hons), "The Relationship between Return on Investment and Quality of Study Methodology in Workplace Health Promotion Programs," *American Journal of Health Promotion 28* (2014): 6, accessed July 4, 2016, doi.org/10.4278/ajhp.130731-LIT-395

142 Ibid.

143 Michael O'Donnel, "What Is the ROI of Workplace Health Promotion? The Answer Just Got Simpler by Making the Question More Complicated," *American Journal of Health*(2014): 28, accessed July 4, 2016, DOI: 10.4278/ajhp.28.6.iv

144 "Hey, How Come Wellness Needs an ROI but Real Healthcare Doesn't?" *They Said What?*, accessed may 22,2017, https://theysaidwhat.net/2015/11/09/hey-how-come-wellness-needs-an-roi-but-real-healthcare-doesnt/

145 Michael P. O'Donnell, M.B.A., M.P.H., Ph.D, "Evaluating Your Health Promotion Program for the Return on Allocated Resources (ROAR) Factor," *American Journal of Health Promotion* 30 (2015): 2, accessed July 4, 2016, doi/pdf/10.4278/ajhp.30.2.v

146 Alfred Lewis, "The Great Debate, Part 4: Ron Goetzel Admits Doctoring Original Documents," accessed December 4, 2016, https://theysaidwhat.net/2016/10/20/the-great-debate-part-4-ron-goetzel-admits-doctoring-original-documents/

147 Alfred Lewis, "The Latest on Nebraska: Ron Goetzel Covers Up His Cover Up," accessed December 4, 2016, https://theysaidwhat.net/2016/09/21/the-latest-on-nebraska-ron-goetzel-covers-up-his-cover-up/

148 Martha Stoddard, "Nebraska's Acclaimed Wellness Program Under Fire," accessed July 4, 2016, http://www.omaha.com/livewellnebraska/nebraska-s-acclaimed-wellness-program-under-fire/article_ccf3e8d8-4348-54e6-bb83-

cca843dcd9a7.html

[149] Alfred Lewis "The Latest on Nebraska: Ron Goetzel Covers Up His Cover Up."

[150] Dr. Steve Aldana, "One of the Nation's Best Wellness Programs," *WellSteps Blog* (July 15, 2016), https://www.wellsteps.com/blog/2016/07/15/the-nations-best-wellness-program/

[151] "Sharon Begley, "Top Wellness Award Goes to Workplace Where Many Health Measures Got Worse," accessed November 5, 2016, https://www.statnews.com/2016/09/27/workplace-wellness-award/

[152] "The Art of Personomics," *John Hopkins Medicine*, accessed July 4, 2017, http://www.hopkinscim.org/breakthrough/summer-2015/the-art-of-personomics/

[153] "Doctors Spend 27% of the Workday With Patients, Study Finds. What Do They Do for the Rest of It?" Advisory Board, accessed July 4, 2017, https://www.advisory.com/daily-briefing/2016/09/08/documentation-time

[154] "Antifragility," *Wikipedia*, accessed July 4, 2017, https://en.wikipedia.org/wiki/Antifragility

[155] Jay Parkinson, "Toward a New Definition of Primary Care: Primary Care 3.0," accessed July 4, 2017, https://blog.jayparkinsonmd.com/2017/06/20/toward-a-new-definition-of-primary-care-primary-care-3-0/

[156] Venu Julapalli, "The Tenets of Health 3.0," accessed July 4, 2017, http://tincture.io/the-tenets-of-health-3-0-516e51e3e89f#.k71j0vv45

[157] "India's Philanthropist-Surgeon Delivers Cardiac Care Henry Ford-Style," *NPR: Boise State Public Radio*, accessed July 4, 2016, http://www.npr.org/sections/goatsandsoda/2015/01/05/375142025/india-s-philanthropist-delivers-cardiac-surgery-henry-ford-style

[158] Katie Thomas, "His Doctors Were Stumped. Then He Took Over," *The New York Times*, accessed July 4, 2017, http://mobile.nytimes.com/2017/02/04/business/his-doctors-were-stumped-then-he-took-over.html

[159] Lena Sun, "Burnout Increasing among U.S. Doctors," accessed July 4, 2016, https://www.washingtonpost.com/news/to-your-health/wp/2015/12/08/burnout-increasing-among-u-s-doctors/; "Physicians Have the Highest Suicide Rate of Any Profession. So Why Haven't You Heard About It?" Advisory Board, accessed July 4, 2016, https://www.advisory.com/daily-briefing/2014/07/16/physicians-have-the-highest-suicide-rate-of-any-profession-so-why-havent-you-heard-about-it

[160] Jessica Sweeny-Platt, "Can Strong Leadership Boost Engagement?" accessed November 5, 2016, http://insight.athenahealth.com/strong-physician-leaders-key-tackling-change/

[161] Tom Main and Adrian Slywotzky, "Volume-to-Value Revolution," accessed July 4, 2016, http://www.oliverwyman.com/our-expertise/insights/2012/nov/the-volume-to-value-revolution.html

[162] Dave Chase, "Privia Leads $1.2 Billion Primary Care Renaissance Enabling Economic Renewal," accessed July 4, 2016, http://www.forbes.com/sites/davechase/2016/05/05/privia-leads-1-2-billion-primary-care-renaissance-enabling-economic-renewal

[163] Dave Chase, "Hospital CEOs Behaving Badly and the Devastating Consequences on the Middle Class," accessed July 4, 2017, http://www.forbes.com/sites/davechase/2016/08/29/hospital-ceos-behaving-badly-the-devastating-consequences-on-the-middle-class/

[164] Dave Chase, "Healthcare CEOs Making Newspaper Industry Mistakes," accessed July 4, 2016, http://www.forbes.com/sites/davechase/2012/02/09/healthcare-ceos-guide-to-avoiding-newspaper-industry-mistakes

[165] Zubin Damania, "Lose Yourself," accessed July 4, 2017, http://zdoggmd.com/lose-yourself/

[166] Dave Chase, "City Slashes Healthcare Costs by Improving Health Benefits," accessed July 4, 2016, http://www.forbes.com/sites/davechase/2016/02/08/city-slashes-healthcare-costs-by-improving-health-benefits

[167] Bridget C. Booske et al., "County Health Rankings Working Paper: Different Perspectives for Assigning Weights to Determinants of Health," accessed July 4, 2016, https://uwphi.pophealth.wisc.edu/publications/other/different-perspectives-for-assigning-weights-to-determinants-of-health.pdf

[168] Dave Chase, "Economic Development 3.0: Playing the Health Card," accessed January 30, 2017, https://www.linkedin.com/pulse/economic-development-30-playing-health-card-dave-chase

[169] Anna Louie Sussman, "Burden of Health-Care Costs Moves to the Middle Class."

[170] "athenahealth Partners with Affected Florida Community to Combat Zika Virus," athenahealth, accessed July 4, 2017, http://newsroom.athenahealth.com/phoenix.zhtml?c=253091&p=irol-newsArticle&ID=2192379

[171] Bob Kocher, "How I Was Wrong About ObamaCare," accessed July 4, 2017, http://www.wsj.com/articles/i-was-wrong-about-obamacare-1469997311;

Dan Diamond, "Pulse Check: Confessions of an Ex-Regulator on How Government Should Work," accessed July 4, 2016, http://www.politico.com/story/2016/05/confessions-of-an-ex-regulator-farzad-mostashari-on-how-government-should-work-222901

[172] Jonathan Bush, "More Disruption Please," accessed July 4, 2016, http://www.youtube.com/watch?v=rCYaebWQA68&feature=youtu.be&t=8m34s

23378120R00173

Made in the USA
Columbia, SC
12 August 2018